Employee Involvement Team

Leader Manual
and
Instructional Guide

BY
DONALD L. DEWAR

Published by

INTERNATIONAL

QCI INTERNATIONAL
1350 Vista Way
Airport Industrial Park
P.O. Box 1503
Red Bluff, CA 96080 U.S.A.

ACKNOWLEDGMENTS

This second edition is the product of employee participation. The "BaDJer" team is composed of certain QCI International consultants. Meetings are conducted via telephone conference calls. Special thanks to members of the BaDJers:

Jeff Dewar
Jack Lindner
Bernie Perry
Bob Tate
Don Dewar

In addition, several employee involvement facilitators served on an advisory panel. As panelists, they reviewed and commented on the revisions being proposed by members of the BaDJer team. The BaDJers are grateful for the tireless efforts and contributions of these panelists:

Janet K. Atkinson	Boise State University
Corey Mostow	Fel-Pro, Inc.
Marvin Reedy	Cooper Industries
William Sanders	Campbell Soup Co.
John Williams	Avco Electronics/Textron
Mike Snodgrass	Philadelphia Electric
Jim Bryan	Naval Ordnance Station
Fay Iden	R.R. Donnelly & Sons
Ronnie Walker	Texas Instruments
John F. Potts	Tabuchi Electric
Shirley Sneller	Rolscreen

INTRODUCTION

As a team leader, you are one of the most important parts of a movement destined to change the work life of millions of people.

You will guide a gathering of individuals who have heard enough about this concept to make them want to meet with you to learn more about it. The knowledge you impart will transform them into a highly skilled team that can perform with an expertise and precision difficult to believe until you see it in action.

These techniques will enable your people to quickly gather essential data, evaluate it and put it to use skillfully—and logically. Management will not only listen to their recommendations, but also will encourage them to make more.

You will see a marked improvement in communication. Your people will prevent problems whenever possible, and morale will improve significantly. Probably the most satisfying side effect you will experience is that both you and your team will greatly enjoy this activity. Team members who accomplish the most will have the most fun working together!

TABLE OF CONTENTS

GENERAL INFORMATION

You have probably already observed that this book contains some material (such as this page) surrounded by a border. The box is shaded. The manual supplied to members does not contain such material.

A question-and-answer section at the beginning of the member manual reduces the amount of time you must devote to answering questions.

Each chapter in the manual relates to an audiovisual (AV) module. You probably will use both the book and the appropriate AV module to train members.

We have provided both general suggestions for effective training and several detailed meeting agendas to serve as guides. We also have added suggestions for comments, explanations and questions you may use to stimulate member interest and involvement.

This format calls for a certain amount of repetition, which you are sure to ignore as soon as you establish a routine in your team leadership.

Some leaders prefer to handle the narration part of the training modules themselves because this enables them to customize the training by adjusting the rate of information flow to match the learning capabilities of their groups. You may want to do the same or make some other alteration in how these modules are used. However, you will get highly satisfactory results by depending fully on both the audio and visual portions of these modules without deviations of any kind. In fact, unskilled alterations should be avoided since they could prove to be counterproductive.

NOTES

GENERAL INSTRUCTIONAL SUGGESTIONS

The amount of time and attention you give to this part of your manual will depend upon your experience and knowledge. However, even if you are a teacher with top quality credentials, we suggest you read what follows at least once.

Every technique in this manual is included for a solid, practical reason—it has been proven to work. Students taught according to these guidelines will be able to apply them effectively. This will result in a dramatic boost in morale with all the positive side effects that go with it.

Training Aids

Prior to each meeting, be sure to arrange to have available whatever you will need. Here's a list to serve as a reminder:

- The AV training module

- Audiovisual equipment

- Flip chart and marking pens

- Overhead projector

- Blackboard, chalk, eraser

- 35mm slide projector or VCR and monitor

- Tape recorder

Review Questions

There are many ways to ask review questions. However, avoid directing questions to members in turn because they will tend to concentrate their attention only on the questions they will be called upon to answer. Try to be sure that everyone present gets involved in answering each question. To enhance understanding, frequently ask the question, "Why is that?"

Work Sheet Exercises

You might consider using the work sheet at the end of each chapter to stimulate further discussion. Another option is to ask members to complete the work sheet exercises between meetings to facilitate comprehension.

Relate Training to Actual Work Situations

In order to make the subject matter real to members, relate the training modules to their actual work situations. You may be better able than they are to see tie-ins, but encourage members to discover them on their own. This is a very effective way to learn a new concept—a new way of thinking.

Parliamentary Rules of Order

You often will be called upon to be an expert parliamentarian. You will have to make order out of chaos—particularly when member enthusiasm shifts into high gear. This will be especially evident when members vote after a brainstorming session.

Members must always be encouraged to discuss items before they are voted on if they feel the need.

"Stop the AV!"

The manual's leader portion indicates where the AV might be stopped for you to reinforce understanding, emphasize certain points and show tie-ins with actual on-the-job situations. This is important. It's easy for trainees to be diverted by points they don't understand and miss most of what transpires thereafter. As leader, you usually will be able to sense this happening. Therefore, you are strongly urged to stop the AV at any other points you feel necessary during the presentation. You also should encourage members' questions, comments and requests to stop the AV during the presentation of the training module. (We often remind you to do this throughout this book. It's that important!)

Two-way communication maximizes the effectiveness of the training sessions. Encourage it!

An Enjoyable Experience

Your group has an excellent chance to be effective and successful because of the potential that's built into the activity. The concept is based on proven principles of the behavioral and managerial sciences. If the activity is an enjoyable experience, both for you and your members, there is no visible limit to the success you can attain. Make it fun! Draw people out! Get everyone involved! Give attainable assignments! Help members and everyone they work with to win! Your group has great potential, and the concepts of employee participation will bring it out!

HOW DO EMPLOYEE INVOLVEMENT ACTIVITIES AFFECT ATTITUDES?

Opinion surveys taken among leaders and members consistently result in unanimous or near-unanimous agreement that:

- Quality has been improved.
- Morale has been enhanced.
- Problem solving is cost-effective.
- Activities should be continued and extended to others.

WHAT IS THE MANAGEMENT PRESENTATION?

In a management presentation, the leader and members describe their project to their manager and make recommendations on how to solve the problem. Participants use charts they have prepared. This event represents a most exciting form of participation, communication and recognition to all participants.

WHY ARE MANAGEMENT PRESENTATIONS IMPORTANT?

Management presentations promote communication. Members personally inform managers of activities and accomplishments. Members gain recognition for their contributions. Morale is bolstered by this periodic opportunity to deal directly with the manager and to be reassured of support for their activities.

WHEN IS A MANAGEMENT PRESENTATION MADE?

A presentation should be made to:

- Show completed projects.
- Make recommendations.
- Provide status on long-term projects.

WHAT IS THE RECOMMENDED FREQUENCY OF MANAGEMENT PRESENTATIONS?

At least every three months.

WHAT LEADER TRAINING IS PROVIDED?

Leader training is provided often during a concentrated course. The leader then trains members, with help as necessary from the facilitator. Thereafter, additional training is provided only as required or as a refresher.

WHEN ARE MEMBERS TRAINED?

In many companies member training takes place during their meetings over a period of several weeks.

WHAT ARE THE TECHNIQUES?

The most common techniques are those described in this manual. Additional techniques that may serve a team will include, among others, histograms, control charts and scatter diagrams.

NOTES

CASE STUDIES & PROBLEM-PREVENTION TECHNIQUES

INTERNATIONAL

Red Bluff, CA 96080

- Announce the date, time and place of the next meeting.

- Thank attendees for their attention and cooperation.

- Adjourn the meeting.

After Meeting

- Meet with your facilitator to discuss the meeting.

- Follow up to make sure the minutes are completed and distributed.

- If possible, post the agenda for the next meeting in a place easily seen by members.

Case Studies & Problem-
Prevention Techniques

OBJECTIVES

• To review some case studies of team projects.

• To be introduced to several problem-solving techniques.

• To review ways to prevent problems from occurring in the first place.

---

[1]   (Graphic—can be substituted with organization logo)

[2]   (Credits)

CASE STUDIES & PROBLEM-PREVENTION TECHNIQUES

This chapter provides an overview of the group problem-solving process. Several case studies will be used as examples. In addition, we will introduce several problem-prevention techniques.

4

Essentially, this group problem-solving process involves a small group, typically between five and 10 people, which meets regularly to identify, analyze and solve quality problems and other problems in the group's work area.

5

First let's look at an example from the health care field.

6 Members of a problem-solving group in a hospital noticed some equipment in their area that was never used. It had been purchased some time before. No one in the group knew what it was or how to use it.

7 With management's approval, the members arranged to have the manufacturer's representative visit the hospital and talk to the group. They discovered the equipment was quite expensive and very useful. They requested training classes on how to use the equipment. Management approved their request.

8 The result? Existing equipment was brought back into use. Best of all, service to the customer was significantly improved.

STOP THE AV

Ask: How long might this project take?
Expected Answer: A week to four weeks.
Comment: Some organizations refer to small projects like this one as "quick fixes." We might work on several of these during one major project.

9

FOOD SERVICE EXAMPLE

This example is from the food service industry.

CASE STUDIES & PROBLEM-PREVENTION TECHNIQUES

10   Our example is a well-patronized cafeteria that serves food smorgasbord-style. The previous manager was unable to operate the cafeteria at a profit despite its many customers.

11   The current manager encouraged employees to participate in problem solving. A group of employees shocked the manager when they took up the problem "Customer Theft."

12

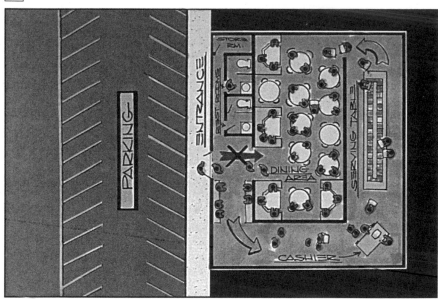

This is an overhead view of the cafeteria layout. At the left is the entrance. Patrons were supposed to follow the curved arrow to the cashier. After paying, they selected their food from the serving table and proceeded into the dining area. Refills were permitted. Thus, people were always moving about. The group found that a number of people were dishonestly taking advantage of the confusion and were proceeding directly into the dining and serving area, per the large straight arrow, without paying.

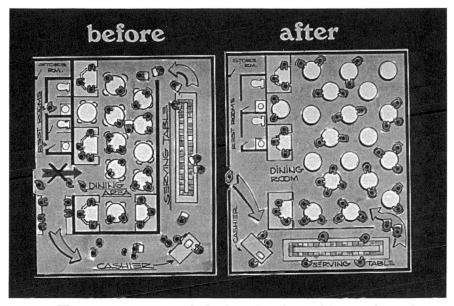

The group recommended relocating the cashier, as shown in the diagram to the right. This prevented people from bypassing the cashier. The employees also suggested moving the serving table (as shown) to permit an expansion of the dining area. A stronger, more competitive business, with greater job security, resulted.

14

Let's now look at an office example.

CASE STUDIES & PROBLEM-PREVENTION TECHNIQUES

29　Members formally present recommended solutions to management. They use the charts and graphs that were developed during every phase of their project. The chapter titled "The Management Presentation" explains how to do this effectively. Most presentations take 15 to 30 minutes. On lengthy projects, the presentation is sometimes used to merely present status.

30

You have seen the process. Let's apply it to an example in a company that produces computers.

31　The company's newest computer is also its hottest-selling computer.

32　The company exports to many overseas customers.

33　The marketing department had become alarmed by the large number of customer complaints.

34　The marketing department traced most errors to packaging and shipping procedures.

35 The shipping department had formed a problem-solving group some time before. Members of the group had been brainstorming for problems to work on. Because of feedback from the marketing department, they added "Excessive Customer Complaints" to the list. Finally, it was selected as the group's project.

36 The group designed a check sheet to collect data about the types of customer complaints. They obtained most of the information from the marketing department.

37

CHECK SHEET		
Damaged	IIII	4
Late	IIII IIII IIII III	18
Missing parts	II	2
Wrong parts	IIII II	7

The completed check sheet looked like this.

38

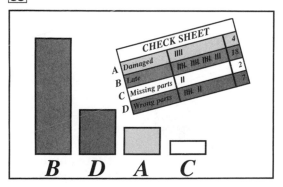

The check sheet data was organized into a Pareto chart. The height of the left column clearly indicated that the most frequent complaint concerned late shipments.

39 The leader had the group do a cause-&-effect analysis on the late shipments problem.

40

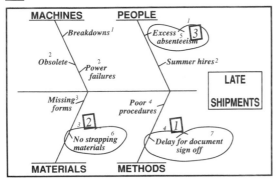

At the completion of the analysis, everyone agreed the principal cause of late shipments was probably the delay which often occurred in obtaining sign-off for various shipping documents.

41 The next step was to verify the principal cause. No one was sure about the best way to do this. Members invited an expert within the company to a meeting to give suggestions.

42

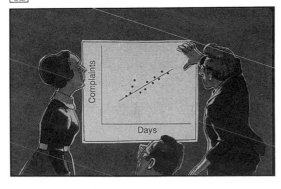

The expert helped members analyze data using several charts they had not yet been trained to use. As the members suspected, the charts showed that delays in document sign-off occurred in nearly all situations for which complaints about late shipments had been received.

43 Finally, members had to come up with a recommended solution. They needed to consider several factors.

44 Company policy required all overseas shipments to be signed off by the shipping department manager. It was very important that the paperwork and crate markings be correct.

45 Mistakes can mean major delays imposed by customs officials of the governments involved. Requirements not only were complex but often were different for each country.

46 The shipping department manager's schedule took him on frequent trips. Shipments would stack up awaiting his return. Even when the manager wasn't traveling, he often was quite difficult to locate.

47 The group made a presentation to the shipping department manager. Using all their charts, they explained step-by-step what they had done to identify, analyze and solve the selected problem.

CASE STUDIES & PROBLEM-
PREVENTION TECHNIQUES

48 The group recommended that at least one person be trained and certified to do the sign-off when the manager was unavailable.

49

To meet the requirement that the manager see all crate markings before shipment, the group recommended creating complete documentation by using an instant camera.

50

	COST	PROBABLE EFFECTIVENESS
BEEPER UNIT	$ 480	MEDIUM
2 WAY RADIO	1904	HIGH
LOUD SPEAKERS	1389	MEDIUM
SIGN-OUT	-0-	MEDIUM

The group also made several recommendations on how to locate the manager whenever he was not away on a trip. He said he would try the no-cost, sign-out method first. If that failed, he would carry a beeper unit.

51 The manager accepted the recommendations and congratulated the members for a job well-done.

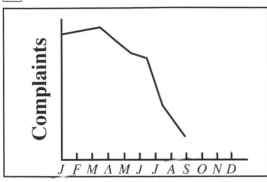

With help from the marketing department, the group kept track of customer complaints for several months after they implemented the changes. To everyone's delight, complaints about late shipments were reduced to nearly zero. This is the follow-up step. Every project should include this step.

52

53 You have just seen some typical examples of what can happen through the group problem-solving process. In upcoming group meetings you will learn to use all of the techniques that these groups used to ensure project success.

54

PROBLEM PREVENTION

The rest of this chapter deals with problem-prevention techniques.

Leader's Note: The next section of this chapter discusses problem-prevention techniques. If your group will not be involved with prevention projects for some time, you might consider saving this section for review at a later time.

CASE STUDIES & PROBLEM-PREVENTION TECHNIQUES

55   Initially, your group will spend time solving problems. You'll be "putting out fires."

56   But a later phase, problem prevention, can bring even greater benefits.

57   Taking simple precautions can help you avoid future problems.

58

A vaccination is a familiar problem-prevention technique.

59   Many techniques help prevent problems at work. Let's review a few of them.

60 Training in special skills allows employees to prevent problems by doing the job right the first time.

61

Putting instructions
in writing helps every-
one avoid mistakes.

62 Using a checklist accomplishes the same thing. Employees don't miss any steps and they do them in the proper order.

CASE STUDIES & PROBLEM-
PREVENTION TECHNIQUES

72   A technique called potential problem analysis also can prevent errors. This technique identifies key points in any process that could go out of control.

73   Then, an alternative approach can be established for use in such an event. This helps avoid unpleasant surprises.

74   The truth about problem prevention is simple. By taking common-sense precautions now, we can avoid enormous problems later.

SUMMARY SHEET

Case Studies & Problem-Prevention Techniques

Problem-Solving Steps

Common Problem-Solving Tools

1. Identify problems.

Brainstorming

2. Select project.

Voting
Discussion
Criteria

3. Collect data.

Sampling
Check sheets
Checklists
Drawings

4. Analyze data.

Pareto
Cause-&-effect analysis

5. Develop solutions.

Brainstorming

6. Pick best solution(s).

Voting
Discussion
Criteria

7. Implement solution(s).

Management presentation

8. Follow up.

Sampling
Check sheets
Checklists
Drawings

Other Key Points

. Members can understand the process better by reviewing projects completed by other groups.

. Groups that use the problem-solving steps and techniques on page 41 will be more successful in completing projects.

. Members should look for opportunities to prevent problems as well as to solve them.

The next page shows a Milestone Chart as it might appear at the end of the group's first meeting. Note the indication that the "Case Studies & Problem-Prevention Techniques" chapter was completed on schedule. Note also that "Group Name," "Code of Conduct" and "Group Recorder" are indicated as having started since members have been asked to begin considering these items.

The chart also shows the group has not yet estimated when they will finish selecting the group name and the code of conduct; the ends of the lines on these milestones indicate times estimated as "not sooner than." In most cases, group members can accurately predict these completions by the end of the second meeting. Likewise, within the first few meetings, most groups will be able to estimate the start of "List Problems" and "Select Project."

MILESTONE CHART

○ = Planned Start

● = Actual Start

△ = Planned Completion

▲ = Actual Completion

MILESTONES	1	2	3	4	5	6	7	8	9	10	11	12
Chapter 1	▲											
Chapter 2		△										
Chapter 3			△									
Chapter 4				△								
Chapter 5					△							
Chapter 6						△						
Chapter 7							△					
Chapter 8								△				
Group Name	●											
Code of Conduct	●											
Group Recorder	●	△										
List Problems												
Select Project												

(Header over columns 1–12: MEETING)

NOTES

Example Code-of-Conduct Statements

Many groups find it helpful to develop a Code of Conduct which includes rules or guidelines all members agree to follow. Statements other groups have used include:

- Attend all group meetings and be on time.

- Listen to and respect the views of other members.

- Criticize ideas, not members.

- Accept results of group votes.

- Everyone is equal during team meetings.

- The only stupid question is the one that isn't asked.

- Carry out assignments on schedule.

- Give credit to whom credit is due.

- Show appreciation to non-members who give assistance.

- Avoid criticism and sarcasm toward other members' ideas.

- No disruptive side conversations.

- Always strive for win-win situations.

- Don't belittle the ideas or opinions of others.

- Before you criticize, give praise and honest appreciation.

Use the previous page to reword some of these statements or to create others you think your group should consider.

NOTES

WORK SHEET EXERCISES

1. People who work with you will be asking, "What is an employee involvement team and how does it operate?"

   Assignment

   In 100 words or less, describe this activity to someone who is unfamiliar with it.

2. Problem prevention is extremely important to ensure constant improvement in quality, cost and attitudes.

   Assignment

   From the information presented in this section, describe one problem-prevention technique you can utilize on your job.

NOTES

REVIEW QUESTIONS

1. A common way to identify problems to work on is
   _____.

2. Problem analysis for the group is the responsibility of the leader and members. May they request the help of others such as staff personnel?

   Yes _____   No _____

3. Members select the problem they will work on.

   True _____   False _____

4. The basic techniques must be significantly modified before being used by non-manufacturing employees.

   True _____   False _____

5. The title usually given to the person providing the overall coordination is _____.

6. The management presentation is sometimes used to merely show status of an ongoing project.

   True _____   False _____

7. A decision-analysis technique called Pareto identifies the major problem. What technique then locates the cause of that problem?

   _____

8. Name at least three techniques used by problem-solving groups:

   1._____

   2._____

   3._____

9. Give an example of how a checklist can assist in preventing problems:

_____

_____

_____

10. Members should not engage in problem-prevention techniques until all their obvious problems have been solved.

   True _____   False _____

11. A way to limit errors if a key point in a process goes out of control is to have a backup plan ready to immediately put into effect. Does a hospital's use of a backup electrical generator qualify as an example of this?

   Yes _____   No _____

12. Name six problem-prevention techniques:

   1._____

   2._____

   3._____

   4._____

   5._____

   6._____

NOTES

NOTES

ANSWERS TO REVIEW QUESTIONS

1. Brainstorming

2. Yes. In fact, it is encouraged.

3. True

4. False. They are effective in a broad variety of work situations.

5. Facilitator or coordinator

6. True. Especially when the project has been underway for some time and is still far from completion.

7. Cause-&-effect analysis

8. Answers include: brainstorming; sampling; data-collection formats such as checklists, check sheets and drawings; graphs; Pareto analysis; cause-&-effect analysis; management presentations; histograms; control charts; scatter diagrams; and stratification.

9. Numerous examples can be used. An obvious one is the checklist that airline flight crews use prior to takeoff to ensure all systems are operating correctly.

10. False

11. Yes

12. Answers include:
    - Additional training
    - Use of detailed work instructions
    - Use of workmanship samples
    - Use of photographs as a guide
    - "Buddy checks"
    - Updating of job instructions
    - Careful examination of incoming parts and/or paperwork
    - Traceability

- Providing gauges to allow employees to check their own work
- First-article examinations to ensure the first of a series of identical units is perfect before making the remainder
- Regular calibration of machines and gauges

Other factors contribute to problem prevention. These include:
- Absenteeism reduction
- Collection of defect data
- Histograms
- Construction of control charts and other charts to provide feedback to group members
- Participation in brainstorming sessions that discuss problem prevention

BRAINSTORMING

INTERNATIONAL
Red Bluff, CA 96080

MEETING NOTES

Brainstorming

Prior to Meeting

- Review pages 59 through 84 of this chapter.

- Confer with facilitator.

- Post final agenda. A suggested agenda follows:

AGENDA
(Date)

Opening Activities
- Minutes.
- Status of action items.
- Review last training topic.
- Review milestone chart.

Today's Training Topic
- Review objectives.
- Present AV.

Discussion
- Review brainstorming rules.
- Review brainstorming steps.
- Discuss work sheet/review questions.
- Conduct practice exercise.

Closing Items
- Review action items.
- Set next meeting's agenda.

During Meeting

Prior to AV

- Welcome members and introduce guests.

- Review the posted agenda for today's meeting.

- Have the minutes of the last meeting read and approved.

- Ask for status report on any action items from previous meeting.

- Review and discuss the material on "Case Studies & Problem-Prevention Techniques." Discuss any completed work sheet exercises or redo some review questions if helpful.

- Introduce "Brainstorming" as one of the most useful and enjoyable of all team activities. Review objectives listed on page 59. You might have several members read them aloud.

During AV

- Present the AV module, stopping where the manual suggests and elsewhere if helpful.

After AV

- Get maximum involvement in a discussion of the material. Be sure to include a discussion of the steps and rules involved in brainstorming.

- Have the group answer and discuss some or all of the work sheet exercises and review questions at the end of this chapter.

- Review the objectives again. Ask members if they feel the objectives were met.

- Give members a chance to practice what they have learned by conducting a brainstorming session on a non-work-related topic. Some examples might be:

  "Ways to get fleas off a dog"
  "Uses for this thing" (Use any object in the room such as a glass, paper clip, pencil, etc.)
  "Ways to make drivers observe the speed limit"

  Be sure to follow all brainstorming steps. Since this is a practice session, you can stop the brainstorming before everyone passes and then continue with the remaining steps. Encourage members to ask any questions they may have as the group goes through the steps.

- If there is enough time, have members brainstorm a name for the group. However, stop after step 3; do not have the members vote at this meeting. Tell them they will probably complete the name selection at the next meeting. In the meantime, they should be considering the names listed so far and try to think of others as well.

- Remind members to continue working on the Code of Conduct as discussed in the chapter "Case Studies & Problem-Prevention Techniques."

- Update milestone chart.

- Get member input in setting the agenda for the next meeting.

- Ask for volunteers to do action items.

- Suggest members read the chapter "Data-Collecting Techniques" before the next meeting.

- Announce the date, time and place of the next meeting.

- Thank attendees for their attention and cooperation.

- Adjourn the meeting.

After Meeting

- Meet with your facilitator to discuss the meeting.

- Follow up to make sure the minutes are completed and distributed.

- If possible, post the agenda for the next meeting in a place easily seen by members.

Brainstorming

```
+---------------------------------------------------------------+
|                        OBJECTIVES                             |
|                                                               |
|   • To know the benefits of group brainstorming.              |
|                                                               |
|   • To know the value of clearly stating the topic to be      |
|     brainstormed.                                             |
|                                                               |
|   • To be able to brainstorm.                                 |
|                                                               |
|   • To be able to prioritize by discussing and voting.        |
|                                                               |
+---------------------------------------------------------------+
```

1 (Graphic—can be substituted with organization logo)

2 (Credits)

BRAINSTORMING

Brainstorming, explained in its most basic way, is using a group of people to stimulate the production of ideas.

4   It is almost always more effective than trying to generate ideas alone.

5   The effectiveness of brainstorming in unlocking a group's creative power has long been recognized.

6   Brainstorming involves several steps. **Step 1.** Define the topic to be brainstormed. For instance, members can use this technique to determine what problems exist in their work area.

60

2-2

7   Members must be as specific as possible in stating the topic to be brainstormed. Calling it "problems within our work area" is a big improvement over calling it "problems." That is much too general.

8

This represents an even further improvement in stating the topic clearly and precisely. The topic should be written at the top of a large sheet of paper so everyone can see it.

9   **Step 2.** The person conducting the session reviews the rules of brainstorming with the group. These rules include:

10

Each member, in rotation, is asked to give an idea.

11 Each member offers only one idea per turn, regardless of how many he or she has in mind.

12 Strive for quantity of ideas to maximize the effectiveness of the team process.

13

Not everyone has an idea during each rotation. When this occurs just say "Pass."

14 No idea should be treated as stupid. Criticizing or belittling someone will curtail the creativity of team members.

15

This may be the first time some members have spoken out during a brainstorming session. It may take courage for them to start. Be patient so as to welcome and encourage participation.

16   Good-natured laughter and informality should be encouraged to enhance the climate for creativity. On the other hand, negative laughter will have an unwelcome and dampening effect.

17

Exaggeration should be encouraged. It may add humor and stimulate greater creativity.

18   The rules of brainstorming should be posted so every member can see them. After the rules have been explained, the group is ready to move on to brainstorming for ideas.

19 **Step 3.** As each member offers an idea, it is written on the sheet of paper. Sometimes, a lengthy idea may have to be shortened into a few words. That's OK, but the person who gave the idea must agree with the abbreviation. The abbreviation must contain enough information so the idea can be understood and discussed later when brainstorming has been completed.

20

The rule prohibiting discussion during brainstorming applies to everyone, including the leader and writer. The rule also prohibits positive comments as well as negative. For instance, saying something like, "Hey, that's good!" is not allowed. No comments, please.

STOP THE AV

Ask: Why must any kind of evaluation be prevented during the brainstorming process?

Answers: 1. To avoid dampening the creative spirit of the group.
          2. To maximize the quantity of ideas received.

---

21 Brainstorming can be speeded up if one person writes the ideas while another makes sure everyone takes a turn in the right order. Having several blank sheets of paper taped up and ready to use also can save time, since one sheet normally is not enough.

22 Step 3 has been completed when all ideas have been recorded and everyone has said "Pass." Depending on the situation, this could take just a few minutes, or it could take an entire meeting or more.

23 **Step 4.** Members quickly evaluate the ideas on the brainstorming list to determine those which appear to have the most merit. In the interest of time, a simple voting technique is used. It works because members are experts in their area. A vote is taken on each idea. The writer records the number of votes next to the idea. During this first round of voting, members may vote for as many ideas as they feel have value. Only supporting votes are taken—no one is asked to vote against an idea.

24

During this step, members can ask for clarification of an idea as it comes up for voting. This is not the time, however, to fully debate the pros and cons of each item. That will occur in the next step. Once this first round of voting has been completed, the ideas which received the most votes should be circled. Members decide how many of the top ideas will be circled.

25

Step 5. All of the items circled in step 4 are discussed and evaluated in detail. The main purpose of this step is to give all members a chance to fully understand the circled items and to consider the relative merits of each. A member can lobby for or against an idea. Others may join in if they wish.

26 **Step 6.** A final vote is taken on all the circled items. This occurs only after those items have been discussed. For this round, usually only one vote per member is permitted.

27 Again, the writer should record the results of the second vote next to the appropriate circled idea. To avoid confusion, different colors should be used to indicate the different votes. Once all circled items have been voted on, a ranking number should be recorded beside each of them.

[28]   What are some examples of brainstorming topics?

[29]   A Code of Conduct represents the rules by which members want to operate. This topic is sometimes brainstormed by members of a new team after they have held a few meetings.

[30]   New teams usually adopt a group name. This is an excellent topic for a group's first real brainstorming effort. The variety is endless and includes many interesting and creative examples.

31   New groups can use brainstorming to identify the objectives they wish to pursue.

32   Problems and obstacles that affect quality, costs and schedules are excellent subjects for brainstorming. Some will become candidates for future projects.

33

Members should identify problems within their own area of expertise and control. Every team has a long list of such problems. Only after these have been resolved should they consider the possibility of working with that "other" group.

34

Potential

PROBLEM

Analysis

Brainstorming can identify problems that might occur if steps are not taken to prevent them. This is called potential problem analysis.

35 After a problem cause has been identified, members might brainstorm for possible solutions.

36  A number of things should be kept in mind as the group explores the subject of brainstorming.

37 An agenda or similar reminder provided by the leader prior to the meeting will allow members to think about the upcoming brainstorming topic and perhaps prepare several ideas for the meeting.

STOP THE AV

Comment: Just a quick reminder: We'll be using an agenda at all meetings. I'll be asking for your help in preparing them.

BRAINSTORMING

38  As mentioned earlier, large sheets of paper should be used for brainstorming. Everyone can read them, and they become a permanent record that can be used for the presentation to management.

39 An overhead projector can be used instead of large sheets of paper. Transparent sheets are easily stored and can also be used in the presentation to management.

40 A blackboard is a very poor alternative. Everyone can see the ideas, but they can easily be erased.

41 A note pad should not be used. Not everyone can see it, and it is not suitable for the presentation to management.

42

Short phrases reviewed at the start of brainstorming can prompt members to be more creative. "Look to nature!" is an example. Many ideas found in nature can be adapted for other uses. Like brainstorming rules, these phrases can be posted on the meeting room wall to serve as reminders.

43   "Think big!" is another example. The creation of small airplanes led to visions of larger aircraft.

44

"Combine!" Combining two or more ideas on the brainstorming list may lead to new and exciting ones. Such was the case when the steam engine and the paddle wheel were joined to power early ships.

45 "Pretend!" A shot of fantasy can help remove the bonds that prevent us from thinking creatively. An example is to imagine the laws of gravity can be cancelled.

46

Or when you brainstorm for solutions, pretend money is absolutely no obstacle. Perhaps something like that happened when the Great Wall of China was conceived.

47 Or pretend you're someone or something else. For instance, dentists might imagine they are bacteria so they can learn how to break through tooth enamel to cause decay.

48 "Think small!" This often leads to new and superior products that cost less. Such was the case with transistor radios and pocket calculators.

49 Creativity during brainstorming can be stimulated if members ask themselves questions based upon the "five W's and one H": What, Why, When, Where, Who and How.

50

Often an incubation period between steps 3 and 4 can increase the effectiveness of brainstorming. Members set aside the list of ideas, usually until the next meeting.

51 During the incubation period, members probably will think of additional ideas. If possible, the list should be posted in the work area or some other location to which members have frequent access.

52 Members and non-members should be encouraged to add ideas to the posted brainstorming chart at any time. After the incubation period, the brainstorming process continues with step 4, the first round of voting.

BRAINSTORMING

53   If visitors drop in during a brainstorming session, they may be invited to join in. If so, the rules should be explained to avoid possible confusion and embarrassment.

54   Members may be asked to help with such tasks as leading the brainstorming session, writing ideas, counting votes and so on. Such additional participation should be encouraged.

55   The group should get in the habit of identifying, on the brainstorming sheets, who was involved and when it happened. Such information is vital for the analysis to have any historical value.

SUMMARY SHEET

Brainstorming

Definition

Groups use brainstorming to develop a list of ideas concerning a predetermined topic.

Basic Brainstorming Procedures

Step 1. Clearly define the topic to be brainstormed.
Step 2. State the rules of brainstorming.
Step 3. Brainstorm and record ideas.
Step 4. Conduct first round of voting.
Step 5. Discuss circled items (pro and con).
Step 6. Conduct second round of voting.

Rules of Brainstorming

* Take turns in rotation.
* Only one idea per person per turn.
* Strive for quantity of ideas.
* Say "Pass" if no idea.
* No criticism.
* Be patient.
* Good-natured laughter is OK.
* Exaggeration is encouraged.

Other Key Points

A. In step 2, brainstorming rules should be stated prior to every brainstorming session, even for experienced groups. Post the rules in the meeting room as a reminder.

B. Record brainstorming ideas on large sheets of paper. Overhead projectors can be used. Avoid blackboards or note pads.

NOTES

WORK SHEET EXERCISES

1. You are about to lead a brainstorming session. You know several steps must be followed. These include (not in correct order):

    *   Brainstorm and record ideas.
    *   Clearly define the topic to be brainstormed.
    *   Discuss circled items (pro and con).
    *   State the rules of brainstorming.
    *   Conduct first round of voting.
    *   Conduct second round of voting.

    Assignment

    Arrange the steps above in the order in which they should occur. Add at least one sentence of explanation to each step.

2. Brainstorming works best when certain rules are followed. These should always be stated in step 2 prior to the actual brainstorming for ideas.

    Assignment

    Summarize in just a few words each of the eight brainstorming rules.

3. Brainstorming can be useful in many situations involving your family, club, church or other groups.

Assignment

Conduct a brainstorming session on your own. It should take only a few minutes. Briefly describe the experience and how you felt about it.

REVIEW QUESTIONS

1. In actual practice, it is not necessary to repeat the rules of brainstorming for every brainstorming session.

    True _____   False _____

2. During brainstorming, it is not essential to write down every idea that is suggested because many are obviously unrelated to the brainstorming topic.

    True _____   False _____

3. During brainstorming, a member can suggest two or more ideas per turn if they are closely related.

    True _____   False _____

4. During brainstorming, members take turns in rotation around the table in suggesting ideas.

    True _____   False _____

5. Laughter of any sort must be avoided during brainstorming.

    True _____   False _____

6. If a member strongly disagrees with an idea offered by another member, the brainstorming session should be halted briefly to discuss why the member disagrees.

    True _____   False _____

7. If the team size is excessively large (for example, 18 members), the team can select a limited number of brainstorming participants to keep things moving fast.

    True _____   False _____

8. Brainstorming is used only to select new projects for the group to pursue.

    True _____   False _____

9. During brainstorming, it is best to write ideas on:

    a. a note pad

    b. large sheets of paper

    c. a blackboard

    d. overhead projector sheets

10. During brainstorming, the person recording the ideas should always take a turn.

    True _____   False _____

11. Normally, visitors at the meeting should be invited to take part in the brainstorming session.

    True _____   False _____

12. When members say "Pass," they give up the chance to take part in the brainstorming from that point on.

    True _____   False _____

13. Name several situations in which the brainstorming technique can be used:

    1. _____

       _____

    2. _____

       _____

    3. _____

       _____

    4. _____

       _____

ANSWERS TO WORK SHEET EXERCISES

1. Steps in Brainstorming

- Clearly define the topic to be brainstormed.

- State the rules of brainstorming.

- Brainstorm and record ideas.

- Conduct first round of voting.

- Discuss circled items (pro and con).

- Conduct second round of voting.

2. Rules of Brainstorming

- Take turns in rotation.

- Only one idea per person per turn.

- Strive for quantity of ideas.

- Say "Pass" if no idea.

- No criticism.

- Be patient.

- Good-natured laughter is OK.

- Exaggeration is encouraged.

NOTES

ANSWERS TO REVIEW QUESTIONS

1. False. Repeating the rules of brainstorming takes just a few minutes and serves as a needed reminder.

2. False. All ideas should be recorded. No judgment should be made on how each idea relates to the topic being brainstormed. This will occur later during voting and discussion.

3. False

4. True

5. False. Good-natured laughter can spur creative thinking.

6. False

7. False. It would be preferable to divide into two groups. If this cannot be accomplished easily, ask if one or two members will help the leader by writing ideas as they are called out.

8. False

9. b. Large sheets of paper. Not only can everyone easily see the ideas, they also have a permanent record of them.

10. True. The writer should offer ideas or pass just as everyone else in the group does.

11. True. However, for some topics, they would not take part in the voting. For example, visitors might suggest possible names for the group, but not vote to select one.

12. False. After a member passes, he or she continues to participate. In future turns, this member may offer an idea or pass again. Everyone continues to participate until everyone has passed.

13.　1. Choosing a team name

2. Identifying group objectives

3. Identifying possible projects

4. Identifying potential problems

5. Identifying possible causes of problems

6. Identifying possible solutions

DATA-COLLECTING TECHNIQUES

INTERNATIONAL

Red Bluff, CA 96080

MEETING NOTES

Data-Collecting Techniques

Prior to Meeting

- Review pages 93 through 124.

- Confer with facilitator.

- Post final agenda. A suggested agenda follows:

AGENDA
(Date)

Opening Activities
- Minutes.
- Status of action items.
- Review last training topic.
- Review milestone chart.

Today's Training Topic
- Review objectives.
- Present AV.

Discussion
- Terms and definitions.
- Random number exercise.
- Sample-size exercise.
- Review questions.

Closing Items
- Review action items.
- Set next meeting's agenda.

During Meeting

Prior to AV

- Welcome members and introduce guests.

- Review the posted agenda for today's meeting.

- Have the minutes of the last meeting read and approved.

- Ask for status report on any action items from previous meeting.

- Review and discuss the material on "Brainstorming." Discuss the work sheet. Asking several review questions helps review the lesson quickly.

- Introduce "Data-Collecting Techniques." Review objectives listed on page 93. You might have several members read them aloud.

During AV

- Present the AV module, stopping where the manual suggests and elsewhere if helpful.

- NOTE: There is a hands-on exercise during the narration of frame #41. Some helpful hints for this important exercise are given on pages 88-91.

After AV

- This lesson allows members to get some hands-on involvement and have some fun. First, discuss the material that has been covered.

- Complete the random number exercise on pages 113 and 114.

- Have the group answer and discuss some or all of the review questions at the end of this chapter.

- Review the objectives again. Ask members if they feel the objectives were met.

- If there is time, continue to work on a group name.

- Remind the group to be thinking about their Code of Conduct.

- Update milestone chart.

- Get member input in setting the agenda for the next meeting.

- Ask for volunteers to do action items.

- Suggest members read the chapter "Data-Collection Formats Plus Graphs" before the next meeting.

- Announce the date, time and place of the next meeting.

- Thank attendees for their attention and cooperation.

- Adjourn the meeting.

After Meeting

- Meet with your facilitator to discuss the meeting.

- Follow up to make sure the minutes are completed and distributed.

- If possible, post the agenda for the next meeting in a place easily seen by members.

LEADERS, PLEASE NOTE: There is a hands-on exercise after frame #41. Stop the audiovisual presentation at that time and let each member do the exercise. Assist anyone who has difficulty with the graph.

The completed frequency distribution should look like Figure 5. Display this completed distribution either on a flip chart or an overhead transparency.

Sketch a line around the tops of the bars as you see in Figure 6. By this time, the members should have a clear idea of what a frequency distribution is.

This exercise is fun and should encourage discussion. The following information may be helpful to you if it does.

Some members look at the bell-shaped figure in frame #41 and cannot make sense out of it. If you tell them the bell-shaped curve is also a normal frequency distribution or is similar to a histogram (both statements are correct), they probably will remain confused.

A simple example will quickly convey the concept. You need a blackboard or a sheet of paper to explain it.

It goes like this:

Imagine a factory manufacturing bars of soap. Each lot contains 1,000 bars. Each bar is supposed to weigh 100 grams. From the lot, collect a sample of 50 bars. Weigh each one. Most bars will weigh 100 grams, but many bars will weigh more or less. Those that weigh 100 grams should be stacked one on top of the other as in Figure 1.

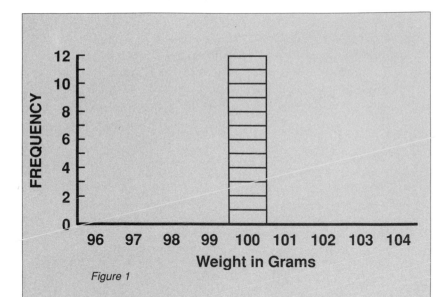

Figure 1

Bars that weigh 101 grams should be stacked next to them. At this point, the leader adds another column to the chart so it looks like Figure 2.

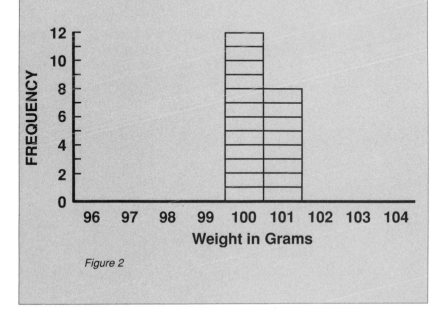

Figure 2

A few bars probably will weigh 102 grams. Add another column to reflect this as in Figure 3.

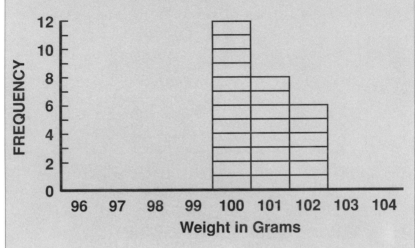

Figure 3

Continue for bars weighing even more as in Figure 4.

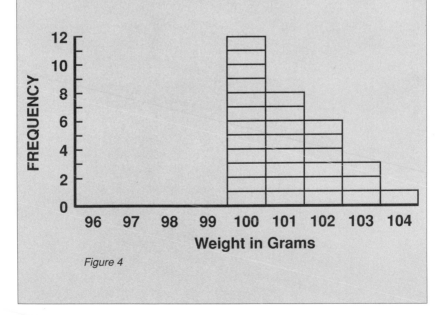

Figure 4

Next, do the same for bars weighing less than 100 grams. By the time all bars in the sample have been stacked, the chart looks like Figure 5.

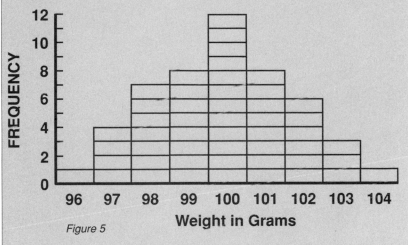

Figure 5

At this point the leader can sketch in a line along the edge of the bars like in Figure 6.

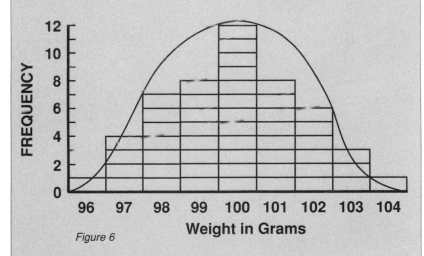

Figure 6

This same example of stacking the sample could be just as easily done with all the bars in the lot. In fact, under normal conditions, both would be similarly bell-shaped. The only difference would be the size of the two stacks.

NOTES

Data-Collecting Techniques

OBJECTIVES

- To know the three types of sampling.

- To know the value of collecting accurate data.

- To be able to select a random sample.

---

1   (Graphic—can be substituted with organization logo)

2   (Credits)

DATA-COLLECTING TECHNIQUES

This introduction to data gathering will explain a variety of techniques for collecting the data that your group must have to solve problems.

There are three basic purposes for collecting data:
1. Problem solving.
2. Problem prevention. This might also be referred to as control.
3. Decision making.

To solve a problem, group members must first analyze it. To analyze it, they must first gather information. This may seem obvious, but many groups find they cannot successfully complete their project simply because they did not collect enough data.

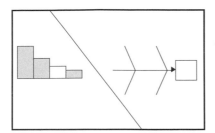 Pareto charts and cause-&-effect diagrams are two major tools used in problem solving.

7 Data can also be used to prevent product or service problems.

8 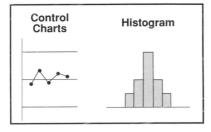 Control charts and histograms use data to keep processes under control. If the process is under control, the product or service will also be predictable. Samples are usually used to plot these charts.

STOP THE AV

Comment: Control charts and histograms are special forms of basic data-gathering techniques we may use in the future. You will see them several times in the basic training. We are building a foundation. If you want to learn more about them, please see me after the meeting.

DATA-COLLECTING
TECHNIQUES

9 How is data related to decision making? We have all heard the expression "calculated risk." Without data, we can only guess. With well-chosen data, we can minimize the risks of incorrect decisions.

10 Why sampling? Sampling reduces the time spent gathering data.

11 When time is saved, money is also saved.

12  Why not just inspect every product or service? Sometimes 100-percent inspection is not as accurate as sampling. Fatigue can reduce a person's attention to detail.

STOP THE AV

Write the following sentence on a flip chart or chalkboard. It is important to write it, as it is shown, on three lines.

Federal fuses are the
result of years of study
and of scientific research.

Give the group 30 seconds to count the number of f 's in the sentence. Ask, "How many found three?" Then four, then five, then six. Show them there are six. Several members probably missed the f 's in of.

[13] You probably have noticed several new words in this lesson. Since everyone should speak the same language, we will now define some key items in sampling.

[14] When we say 100-percent examination, we mean we are examining everything. Examination results could be sorted into groups. If we were inspecting a product, we would probably sort the good from the bad. The bad could then be sorted into types of defects. This grouping is called stratifying. This key idea will be developed later.

DATA-COLLECTING
TECHNIQUES

Let us represent the population, or lot, with a large N. The sample is indicated by a small n. In this example, large N represents the barrel of wine, and small n represents the glass.

16 In this lesson, we will cover two types of data: attribute and variable.

17 Attribute data answers a yes-or-no type of question, such as good or bad, on or off, accept or reject. Most attribute data counts something rather than measures it.

18 Variable data consists of measurements. For example, a person's height or weight is variable data. Attribute data is easier to use. Variable data can provide more information.

19 Examples of sampling are common in our everyday life. Television ratings are based on very small and carefully chosen samples.

Pollsters use small samples to determine public opinion. Polls can be quick and remarkably accurate.

21   Only one drop of blood is needed to gain all sorts of information about a person's entire blood supply.

22   Samples are used to test smog levels of cities.

23   An election is a 100-percent examination. All votes are sorted by candidate and counted before the winner is declared.

24   The sampling process allows forecasters to predict results long before all returns have been counted. By using good sampling practices, you can predict the outcome of a national election within plus or minus 5 percent from a sample as small as 400 people.

How many children play soccer in our community? This information need not be as accurate as election data. A sample size of 100 may be large enough. The result will be accurate to within plus or minus 10 percent.

26 What percent of the population has gone ocean surfing? This would again require a sample size of about 100.

27 Some products are destroyed during inspection. This is called destruct testing. Sampling minimizes this product loss.

28

An expensive form of destruct testing is crash-testing new cars. The cost of these tests can be reduced by using variable data. The tester measures the exact amount each part moves. This provides much more information than simply counting good or bad. Videotaping the crash captures even more data.

29

Sampling has six steps.

30

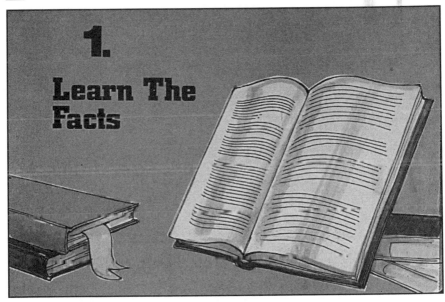

Step 1. Learn the facts. For example, a pollster wants to forecast who will be elected mayor of the city. Some things which must be learned include:

—What groups, ethnic and otherwise, make up the city's population.
—Relative size of each group.
—Average age.
—Employment statistics of each group.
—Past voting trends.

This is an example of stratifying data.

DATA-COLLECTING
TECHNIQUES

Step 2. Learn how large the population is (large N). This is called the lot. In the case of the election, the population is the total number of people eligible to vote.

Step 3. Determine the sample size (small n). Staff can help advise the team on what sample size to use.

33   Actions based on samples always involve risk. As the sample size increases, the risk of error decreases. Here is an example. In coin tosses, you should get 50 percent heads and 50 percent tails, but in only 10 tosses you will probably get three heads and seven tails one time in eight. If you tossed the coin 1,000 times, the result would be much closer to 500 each.

STOP THE AV

Ask: Why might team members call in an expert when gathering data on a sampling basis?

Answers: 1. It might save time.
2. It adds credibility to the analysis.
3. Members might learn something new.

The following chart illustrates the probability of getting heads in 10 coin tosses. It is printed in the member manual. You may find it helpful to discuss the chart with the group.

Number of heads in 10 tosses	Probability
0	.1%
1	1.0%
2	4.4%
3	11.7%
4	20.5%
5	24.6%
6	20.5%
7	11.7%
8	4.4%
9	1.0%
10	.1%
	100% Total

Note: This chart is not on the audiotape.

© 1991 QCI INTERNATIONAL
REPRODUCTION PROHIBITED

103
3-11

DATA-COLLECTING
TECHNIQUES

Step 4. Select the sample. The pollster must find what voters would form a representative sample. The sample must contain the correct proportion of voters from all major groups. This is called a stratified sample. If there are too many or too few from any group, the sample is biased and the result may be wrong.

35 Make sure the sampling results are not misleading. A badly selected sample could cause a bad decision to be made.

36

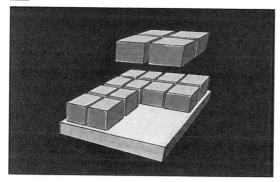

Bias is a common problem in sampling. Bias means favoring one part of the lot over the rest. This is an example of bias. This sample was selected from one portion of the lot instead of being selected at random.

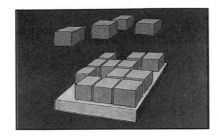

37

The likelihood of bias is dramatically reduced when the sample is drawn at random from all parts of the lot. Random number tables provide the best way to select a random sample.

38

Accessibility ensures random sampling and avoids bias. There is a right and a wrong way to do this.

39

Step 5. Evaluate the sample by measuring or testing each sample unit for the characteristic feature you are studying. In a poll, each person in the sample would be asked carefully chosen questions.

DATA-COLLECTING
TECHNIQUES

6.
Make a
Prediction

Step 6. Make a prediction. All sampling involves risk. Sampling allows you to make better decisions about lots that have not been 100-percent checked.

Remember, variable data provides more information than attribute data. Here is an example of this. Without the variable data, we would not know whether to adjust the weight up or down.

STOP THE AV

Have the members use the following data to construct a frequency distribution chart. It is printed in the member manual. Any method of showing the bars is OK as long as they fill in the correct number of spaces in the correct column.

After each member has completed his/her chart, compare the results with those on page 91.

DATA

WT.	FREQ.
95	0
96	1
97	4
98	7
99	8
100	12
101	8
102	6
103	3
104	1
105	0

Figure 7

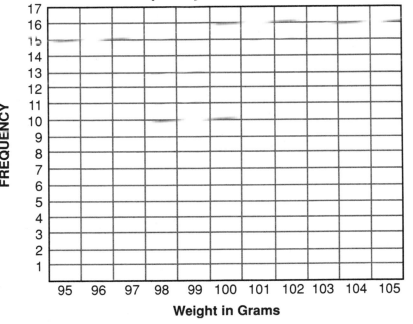

Frequency Distribution Chart

Figure 8

DATA-COLLECTING
TECHNIQUES

42   The three common sampling techniques are:

1. Random selection
2. Systematic selection
3. Stratified selection

43   Random selection requires drawing samples from every part of the lot. Two rules apply:

1. Each unit must have an equal opportunity to be selected.
2. Each unit must be picked independently of any other unit.

44

Systematic sampling uses a planned method for picking units. For example, every fifth unit might be picked. Systematic sampling can provide more information than random sampling—it preserves the order in which the work was performed. Systematic sampling has a built-in bias. When you use this form of sampling, consider this bias in your decision.

STOP THE AV

Ask: How is systematic sampling biased?

Answer: It's not random. Some units will be picked because of their location. Others will be excluded.

---

45 Stratified sampling requires dividing the population into groups, or layers—an excellent way to remove biases. First you should find out what different parts make up the population. In problem solving, the problem frequently occurs only in one area. You cannot solve the problem until you find the area it is in.

46 If a random sample is selected from each layer, or group, the result is a stratified random sample. This is how pollsters accurately predict election results.

47 Here is a brief review of data-gathering techniques.

48 There are three main reasons for gathering data:

1. To solve problems.
2. To prevent problems. This might also be stated as "to control processes."
3. To improve the quality of decisions.

49 Sampling reduces the time and money required to gather data.

© 1991 QCI INTERNATIONAL
REPRODUCTION PROHIBITED

109
3-17

DATA-COLLECTING
TECHNIQUES

|50| The six steps of sampling are:

1. Learn the facts.
2. Learn how large the population is.
3. Determine the sample size.
4. Select the sample.
5. Evaluate the sample.
6. Make a prediction.

|51| Three common types of sampling are:

1. *Random*—where each item in the lot has an equal chance to be chosen.
2. *Systematic*—where a pattern of selection is used. An example is selecting every fourth item.
3. *Stratified*—where a portion of each major group in the population is selected.

|52| The techniques in this lesson will help to ensure good solutions.

SUMMARY SHEET

Data-Collecting Techniques

Definition

Data must be collected in order to solve problems. A number of techniques can aid in this task.

Data-Collection Steps

Step 1. Learn the facts.
Step 2. Learn how large the population (N) is.
Step 3. Determine the sample size (n).
Step 4. Select the sample.
Step 5. Evaluate the sample.
Step 6. Make a prediction.

Other Key Points

A. Collecting data has three basic purposes:

 1. Problem solving
 2. Problem prevention
 3. Decision making

B. Three common sampling techniques are:

 1. Random selection
 2. Systematic selection
 3. Stratified selection

C. The two broad categories of data are:

 1. Attribute
 2. Variable

D. Attribute data counts something rather than measures it.

E. Variable data measures some characteristics, such as weight.

F. Small samples, properly chosen, can accurately predict the condition of the entire population.

NOTES

WORK SHEET EXERCISES

1. Frequency Distribution Exercise

A useful way to sample data is to use the frequency distribution. This format uses variable data, which shows more information than a simple tally of good vs. bad.

Assignment

If you have not already done it, refer back to page 3-15. Plot the data from Figure 7 onto the blank graph (Figure 8) on the same page.

What is the shape of the frequency distribution?

2. Random Number Exercise

Write down 10 whole numbers from 0 through 99. The numbers should be selected in some fashion so that your group leader would not have any idea what they might be.

As your leader calls out 10 numbers from the random number chart, call out "hit" if one of your numbers is called.

> **Leader instruction:** After team members have each selected their 10 numbers, drop a paper clip on the random number chart on page 114. Where it lands, note which two-digit number is closest to the small end of the paper clip. From that number, you may go in any direction (up, down, left or right). Call out 10 numbers in a row from that path.

Notice that you could not guess what numbers the leader would pick because he or she picked them randomly. This is how using random numbers can protect against bias. Practice this powerful technique in selecting a sample from your work area.

Your 10 numbers represent 10 percent of the 100 you could have chosen. If these were defects, the lot would be 10-percent defective.

Most people will have at least one number called out of the first 10 the leader calls. When sampling for a "good-bad, or go-no go" type of data, the proportion of each is one factor in selecting sample size. For instance, if the lot is 1-percent bad, a sample of 10 probably won't find any defects.

© 1991 QCI INTERNATIONAL
REPRODUCTION PROHIBITED

113

3-21

DATA-COLLECTING
TECHNIQUES

RANDOM ORDERINGS OF NUMBERS 00-99

15	62 38 72 92	03 76 09 30 75	77 80 04 24 54	67 60 10 79 26
77	81 15 14 67	55 24 22 20 55	36 93 67 69 37	72 22 43 46 32
18	87 05 09 96	45 14 72 41 46	12 67 46 72 02	59 06 17 49 12
08	58 53 63 66	13 07 04 48 71	39 07 46 96 40	20 86 79 11 81
16	07 79 57 61	42 19 68 15 12	60 21 59 12 07	04 99 88 22 39
54	13 05 46 17	05 51 24 53 57	46 51 14 39 17	21 39 89 07 35
95	27 23 17 39	80 24 44 48 93	75 94 77 09 23	48 75 91 69 03
22	39 44 74 80	25 95 28 63 90	41 19 48 46 72	51 12 97 39 83
69	95 21 30 11	98 81 38 00 53	41 40 04 16 78	67 29 83 41 18
75	75 63 97 12	11 57 05 86 52	82 72 47 72 14	37 72 69 75 48
08	74 79 30 80	70 11 66 79 25	88 01 94 52 31	38 57 98 71 62
04	88 45 98 60	90 92 74 77 87	40 18 65 87 37	08 68 62 39 52
97	35 74 05 75	42 13 49 48 38	74 19 06 42 60	20 79 90 81 77
53	09 93 28 29	80 19 68 30 45	94 49 49 71 21	93 93 71 30 34
26	36 68 48 09	37 69 26 22 80	23 34 10 45 70	83 51 07 37 44
49	16 57 15 79	56 63 22 94 28	11 39 69 55 38	53 06 97 20 42
03	51 79 78 74	75 23 73 75 98	47 85 07 26 02	61 28 01 22 16
21	88 87 28 48	23 44 03 03 80	53 89 07 87 93	30 17 84 17 74
56	41 73 33 41	59 16 59 50 98	24 24 87 06 75	99 52 09 88 05
72	39 19 70 17	01 04 01 22 33	04 84 63 27 65	84 39 45 55 31
97	28 25 81 49	71 69 22 04 51	56 46 56 15 10	69 59 99 50 29
18	87 02 72 08	74 52 16 03 82	20 19 66 23 62	37 51 04 89 31
53	40 11 75 45	13 56 85 31 37	09 17 71 96 79	39 50 79 27 62
60	49 03 41 56	78 33 77 28 92	21 90 10 62 01	97 06 45 01 19
09	16 12 75 04	39 69 95 00 48	26 85 28 73 08	66 92 10 66 75
64	20 19 87 54	88 15 12 54 24	06 99 57 07 28	51 34 54 98 50
31	28 07 58 77	03 98 26 76 09	10 44 57 61 28	60 29 85 70 79
80	04 28 47 76	35 73 67 78 28	09 39 88 63 74	41 26 92 42 33
24	60 22 51 19	34 54 08 24 73	86 72 11 44 69	76 90 81 17 85
59	16 11 26 29	18 97 78 44 43	58 92 78 70 80	09 65 32 68 26
58	54 29 98 27	40 51 92 07 13	58 41 59 56 94	16 32 51 42 54
20	18 34 22 73	57 40 67 17 28	63 57 74 36 18	65 55 25 50 68
53	90 46 56 19	50 58 33 84 53	14 74 17 40 73	86 11 04 02 04
97	16 93 94 65	70 95 95 83 20	91 42 57 95 63	00 86 29 02 53
72	55 71 70 92	04 22 53 19 29	67 29 13 56 70	45 73 45 05 04
99	19 72 58 35	49 09 26 00 74	26 42 94 52 02	83 31 85 65 66
48	21 49 72 97	79 19 64 81 82	78 92 51 96 51	28 79 13 20 82
52	37 68 15 53	22 98 30 16 31	83 24 87 69 29	24 85 44 25 50
97	50 52 53 52	26 78 21 68 69	57 79 42 40 89	55 81 75 24 52
36	05 09 18 11	71 01 63 17 60	11 65 19 43 07	44 86 19 58 92
20	79 70 09 30	81 14 53 80 93	71 94 10 18 14	83 69 76 53 25
13	07 89 72 08	00 37 75 14 94	83 85 06 72 66	07 47 30 17 11
94	26 82 37 43	34 23 00 14 50	96 85 41 17 71	69 20 15 98 82
13	55 88 38 43	75 37 43 83 85	53 74 54 62 99	68 93 74 43 95
02	44 24 97 71	97 93 12 70 89	42 52 33 24 91	05 87 53 15 77

REVIEW QUESTIONS

1. Reasons for gathering data include:

   a. To analyze problems
   b. To prevent problems
   c. To make decisions
   d. To show that someone else caused the problem
   e. All of the above

2. Random sampling helps ensure the sample will be representative of the lot.

   True _____   False _____

3. The data you need may already exist. Give one example of a person or organization that might be able to help you find the data.

   _____
   _____
   _____

4. Select the term which generally describes the following: A sample whose average value is different from the average value of the lot.

   a. Population
   b. Random
   c. Bias
   d. Frequency

5. Describe one way a sample might be biased.

   _____
   _____
   _____

6. Can a stratified sample also be a random sample?

   Yes _____   No _____

© 1991 QCI INTERNATIONAL
REPRODUCTION PROHIBITED

115
3-23

DATA-COLLECTING
TECHNIQUES

7. Which of the following depend on first gathering data?

   a. Brainstorming
   b. Control charts
   c. Pareto charts
   d. Histograms

8. Gathering data at predetermined intervals is:

   a. Random sampling
   b. Systematic sampling
   c. Stratified sampling
   d. None of the above

9. As a general rule, the sample size can be reduced as the lot size increases.

   True _____   False _____

10. The foremost reasons for sampling are that it saves time and money.

    True _____   False _____

11. Destruct testing is a form of sampling. Give an example.

   _____

   _____

12. Random sampling can best be ensured by:

    a. Simply remembering to include an equal number of units from all parts of the lot.
    b. Using a table of random numbers to decide which units to pick.
    c. Selecting at predetermined intervals, such as every 30 minutes.

ANSWER TO WORK SHEET EXERCISE 1

1. Frequency Distribution Exercise Answer

The frequency distribution should look like the one shown below. It is in the general form of a bell. Most values are near the center of the distribution.

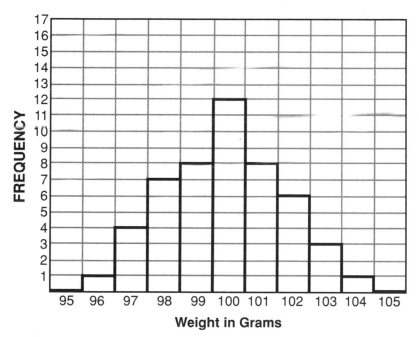

Frequency Distribution Chart   n = 50

Weight in Grams

© 1991 QCI INTERNATIONAL
REPRODUCTION PROHIBITED

117

3-25

DATA-COLLECTING
TECHNIQUES

NOTES

ANSWERS TO REVIEW QUESTIONS

1. a. To analyze problems
   b. To prevent problems
   c. To make decisions

2. True

3. Quality assurance, an operator from another department or any other expert on your project.

4. c. Bias

5. Taking parts only from the top, taking the first production of a shift and taking only one operator's output are all examples of bias.

6. Yes. A random sample could be taken from each part of a stratified sample.

7. b. Control charts
   c. Pareto charts
   d. Histograms

8. b. Systematic sampling

9. False. The sample, as a percent of the lot, decreases as the lot gets larger, but the actual sample size does not.

10. True

11. Crash-testing cars, flame-testing fabric and breaking a steel bar are examples of destruct testing.

12. b. Using a table of random numbers to decide which units to pick.

© 1991 QCI INTERNATIONAL
REPRODUCTION PROHIBITED

119

3-27

DATA-COLLECTING
TECHNIQUES

NOTES

OPTIONAL READING

Sampling and Risk

The Actual Situation

	Good	Bad
Accept	**A** (OK)	**B** (Error)
Reject	**C** (Error)	**D** (OK)

DECISION

The decisions you make based on sampling fall into one of four groups. Two of the decisions are correct. The other two are errors.

The following illustrations demonstrate these four decisions.

EXAMPLE 1

In this example, the sample is in the center of the requirements. Thus, you would predict the population is also in the center of the requirements.

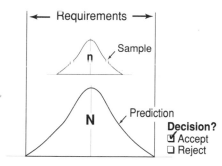

Figure 1a

Checking 100 percent of the population confirms you made the correct decision.

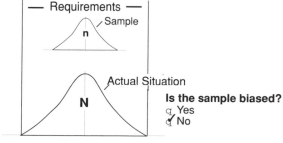

Figure 1b

© 1991 QCI INTERNATIONAL
REPRODUCTION PROHIBITED

121

3-29

DATA-COLLECTING
TECHNIQUES

EXAMPLE 2

This sample is centered just as the sample was in Example 1. You make the same prediction—that the population is also centered.

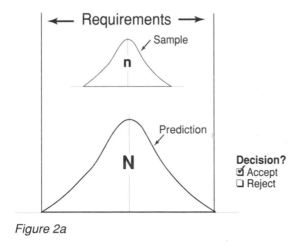

Figure 2a

This time, the 100-percent check of the population reveals it is on the high side of the requirements and part of it is outside of the requirements. The decision was incorrect. The sample was somehow biased.

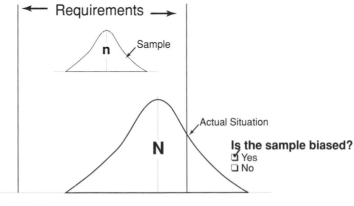

Figure 2b

EXAMPLE 3

In this example, the sample is located in the upper half of the requirements. You would predict the population is aimed at the same place and that part of the population is outside of the requirements.

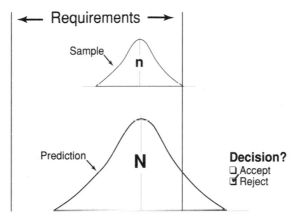

Figure 3a

The 100-percent check reveals the population is actually centered and within the requirements. The biased sample unfortunately caused you to reject an acceptable lot.

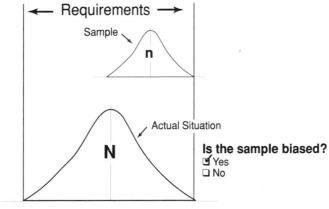

Figure 3b

DATA-COLLECTING
TECHNIQUES

EXAMPLE 4

As with Example 3, the sample is located in the upper half of the requirements. Again, you would predict that the population is aimed at the same place and that part of the population is outside the requirements.

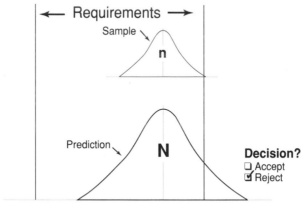

Figure 4a

Checking the entire population, you find the sample was well-chosen. The decision to reject the population was correct.

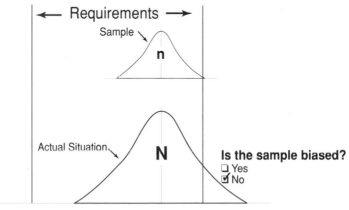

Figure 4b

DATA-COLLECTION
FORMATS
PLUS GRAPHS

INTERNATIONAL

Red Bluff, CA 96080

MEETING NOTES

Data-Collection Formats Plus Graphs

Prior to Meeting

- Review pages 129 through 159 of this chapter.

- Confer with facilitator.

- Post final agenda. A suggested agenda follows:

AGENDA
(Date)

Opening Activities
- Minutes.
- Status of action items.
- Review last training topic.
- Review milestone chart.

Today's Training Topic
- Review objectives.
- Present AV.

Discussion
- Review summary sheet.
- Discuss work sheet/review questions.

Closing Items
- Review action items.
- Set next meeting's agenda.

During Meeting

Prior to AV

- Welcome members and introduce guests.

- Review the posted agenda for today's meeting.

- Have the minutes of the last meeting read and approved.

- Ask for status report on any action items from previous meeting.

- Review and discuss the material on "Data-Collecting Techniques." Discuss any completed work sheet exercises or redo some review questions if helpful.

- Introduce "Data-Collection Formats Plus Graphs." Review objectives listed on page 129. You might have several members read them aloud.

During AV

- Present the AV module, stopping where the manual suggests and elsewhere if helpful.

After AV

- Get maximum involvement in a discussion of the material. Be sure to discuss the summary sheet.

- Have the group answer and discuss some or all of the work sheet exercises and review questions at the end of this chapter.

- Review the objectives again. Ask members if they feel the objectives were met.

- Have members continue to work on developing their Code of Conduct.

- You may be at a point to begin problem selection. Refer to the project selection section on page 11 of Appendix C.

- Update milestone chart.

- Get member input on setting the agenda for the next meeting.

- Ask for volunteers to do action items.

- Suggest members read the chapter "Decision Analysis Using Pareto" before the next meeting.

- Announce the date, time and place of the next meeting.

- Thank attendees for their attention and cooperation.

- Adjourn the meeting.

After Meeting

- Meet with your facilitator to discuss the meeting.

- Follow up to make sure the minutes are completed and distributed.

- If possible, post the agenda for the next meeting in a place easily seen by members.

NOTES

Data-Collection Formats Plus Graphs

OBJECTIVES

- To understand how to save time and effort by collecting data in an organized manner onto carefully designed formats.

- To become familiar with the use of data-collection formats such as checklists, drawings, check sheets and others.

- To become familiar with various kinds of charts and graphs used in data analysis and presentation.

$\boxed{1}$ (Graphic—can be substituted with organization logo)

$\boxed{2}$ (Credits)

DATA-COLLECTION FORMATS PLUS GRAPHS

This chapter has two sections. The first section shows how to construct and use data formats. These are the forms you create to make data collection easy. The second section introduces several kinds of graphs and charts and shows you how to use them.

Members need data to solve problems. They can use different techniques to speed and simplify the collection process. A variety of data-collection formats, designed by members, will help accomplish this goal.

Ways to Collect Data
1. **Checklists**
2. **Drawings**
3. **Check Sheets**

Three time-saving approaches to collecting data needed to solve problems will be studied: (1) checklists, (2) drawings, (3) check sheets.

6 A review of each technique will help ensure understanding. First, a common example of a checklist is a grocery list.

7

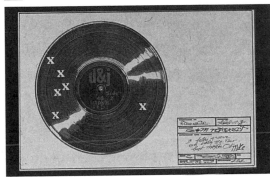

Drawings can be used to show the location of defects, such as on this record.

8

CHECK SHEET

JUNE

ERROR	1	2	3	4	TOTAL
ADDITION	卌	卌 IIII	卌 I	卌 II	27
MULTIPLICATION	卌 卌 卌 IIII	卌 卌 卌 卌 II	卌 卌 IIII	卌 卌 卌	70
OMISSION	III	卌 I	II	I	12
ROUTING	II		I	III	6
TYPING	卌 I	卌	卌 II	卌 II	25
TOTAL	35	42	30	33	140

Check sheets can be used in office, factory or service areas.

DATA-COLLECTION FORMATS
PLUS GRAPHS

9 First, let's look at the checklist—a list of things checked off one by one as they are done.

10 As mentioned earlier, the grocery list is a familiar type of checklist.

11

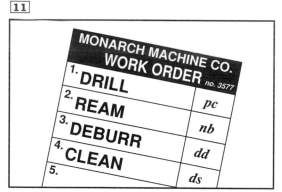

A work order is a form of checklist that ensures each step will be completed and in the correct sequence.

12 Before an airplane takes off, the flight crew uses a lengthy checklist to ensure all systems are working properly.

13 A checklist can help a family remember all the items they need for a successful vacation trip.

14 Creating checklists can be an imaginative process that doesn't always involve writing things on paper.

15

A memory hook is a type of checklist. This is an example of using a key word in which each letter reminds you of an essential task.

16   Another memory hook is "3 M's and a P." They denote four major headings commonly used in cause-&-effect analysis. These are materials, methods, machines and people.

17

Still another memory hook is "5 W's and an H."

STOP THE AV

Ask for examples of checklists used by members in the performance of their duties. Accept examples from non-job-related activities.

*DATA-COLLECTION FORMATS
PLUS GRAPHS*

18 Drawings, the second data-collection format type, can be used to record the exact location of defects or other information. Illustrations and photos can also be used.

19

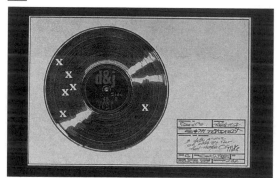

One example is an engineering drawing of a music record disc. The locations of scratches are indicated right on the drawing.

20

A company manufacturing face masks for hockey goalkeepers painted its mask to show the locations where stitches would have occurred if a well-known player had not been protected. Sales went up sharply.

21

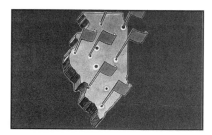

A large marketing organization sticks flag pins in a map to show different levels of sales at its various sales office locations.

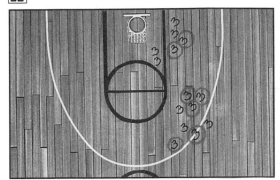

22

Athletic teams use this statistical approach to analyze player effectiveness. Player No. 3 was observed to shoot from one of two general locations. The number "3" was written at the spot he took each shot. If he scored, it was circled. A quick look at the result convinced the player to avoid shooting while in close to the basket.

23 Marketing surveys frequently use aerial photos to determine where shopping centers should be located.

24

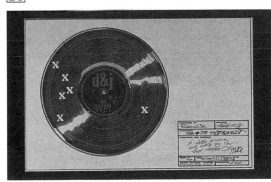

Back to defects. In this illustration, X's show the location of scratches on record discs. This is the result of one day's production.

25 Instead of X's, one could draw the actual shapes of scratches and their locations on the drawing.

DATA-COLLECTION FORMATS
PLUS GRAPHS

Symbols can be used when more than one kind of defect is present. The X's represent scratches, and the squares show the location of pits in the disc.

27 Including these kinds of drawings during the management presentation improves communication.

STOP THE AV

Ask for examples of drawings showing defects used by members either on or off the job.

28

Check Sheets

Members can use check sheets to collect data. A check sheet differs from a checklist because it shows how many times each item occurs. You should follow several steps to make effective check sheets.

29 **Step 1.** Decide on the variety of information you must collect. It is usually a good idea to collect more than you think is necessary. This may result in substantial future savings in time if you need the added data later.

30 **Step 2.** Decide on the time period each check sheet will cover. It may take only a few hours, or it may take days or months.

31

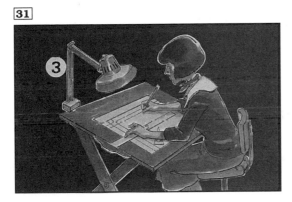

Step 3. Design a form that will help with data collection. Keep a copy of the blank check sheet form. Members may find it to be a good starting point for future projects.

32 **Step 4.** Record the data on the check sheet.

33 Where will you find the data? In an office you might find it by examining records.

137

DATA-COLLECTION FORMATS
PLUS GRAPHS

34 In a factory, the examination of several rejection tags might supply the necessary information for the check sheet. In any area, some of the best data comes from the work area while the problem is happening. Firsthand observation frequently tells you more than secondhand data.

35 So, a check sheet is as useful in the office as the factory. But why collect data? Because it provides the information you need to analyze problems. Often you need the data to build graphs. Graphs will be covered in the second part of this chapter.

36

JUNE			
1	**2**	**3**	**4**
x x x Δ Δ Δ Δ	x x x x x Δ Δ	x x Δ	x x x x x Δ Δ
Legend: x = Addition	T = Typing		
Δ = Multiplication	0 = Omission		
❑ = Routing			

If you need to record a considerable variety of information on one check sheet, you can use symbols. Each "x" represents an error in addition, each "Δ" an error in multiplication.

37

JUNE			
1	**2**	**3**	**4**
x x x Δ Δ Δ Δ ❑ ❑ ❑ T T 00	x x x x x Δ Δ ❑ ❑ T 00000	x x Δ ❑ T T T T 0	x x x x x Δ Δ ❑ ❑ ❑ ❑ ❑ T T T 000
Legend: x = Addition	T = Typing		
Δ = Multiplication	0 = Omission		
❑ = Routing			

Each "❑" is a routing error, each "T" a typing error and each "0" an omission. As shown here, symbols can be used in place of tally marks or numbers when several different types of information are being tallied on one check sheet.

38

CHECK SHEET JUNE					
ERROR	1	2	3	4	TOTAL
ADDITION	𝖳𝖧𝖫	𝖳𝖧𝖫 ////	𝖳𝖧𝖫 /	𝖳𝖧𝖫 //	27
MULTIPLICATION	𝖳𝖧𝖫 𝖳𝖧𝖫 𝖳𝖧𝖫 ////	𝖳𝖧𝖫 𝖳𝖧𝖫 𝖳𝖧𝖫 𝖳𝖧𝖫 //	𝖳𝖧𝖫 𝖳𝖧𝖫 ////	𝖳𝖧𝖫 𝖳𝖧𝖫 𝖳𝖧𝖫	70
OMISSION	///	𝖳𝖧𝖫 /	//	/	12
ROUTING	//		/	///	6
TYPING	𝖳𝖧𝖫 /	𝖳𝖧𝖫	𝖳𝖧𝖫 //	𝖳𝖧𝖫 //	25
TOTAL	35	42	30	33	140

True, this requires more space than the one using symbols, but it is generally easier and less confusing to use.

39

Liters	Tally
11.1 — 12.0	///
10.1 — 11.0	𝖳𝖧𝖫 𝖳𝖧𝖫 /
9.1 — 10.0	𝖳𝖧𝖫 𝖳𝖧𝖫 𝖳𝖧𝖫 𝖳𝖧𝖫
8.1 — 9.0	𝖳𝖧𝖫 𝖳𝖧𝖫
7.1 — 8.0	//

A specialized type of check sheet allows the collection of information that can easily be used to construct a tally sheet. It should be used when repeating the same measurement on identical units.

40

Liters	Tally
11.1 — 12.0	///
10.1 — 11.0	𝖳𝖧𝖫 𝖳𝖧𝖫 /
9.1 — 10.0	𝖳𝖧𝖫 𝖳𝖧𝖫 𝖳𝖧𝖫 𝖳𝖧𝖫
8.1 — 9.0	𝖳𝖧𝖫 𝖳𝖧𝖫
7.1 — 8.0	//

This tally sheet looks like a bar chart. This becomes even more apparent if you imagine a dotted line along the end of the tally marks.

DATA-COLLECTION FORMATS PLUS GRAPHS

41 With luck, the computer can serve as a fast and reliable way to gather check sheet information.

42 Before you design a check sheet and spend time collecting data, you should ask appropriate staff personnel for advice. They may already have collected the necessary data.

STOP THE AV

Request examples of check sheets used by members, either on or off the job.

Be sure members know the difference between a check sheet (like frame #8) and a checklist (like frame #11).

---

43 Checklists, drawings and check sheets members prepare are used during problem analysis and again during presentations to management.

44 You have just seen three data-collection formats. While you may want to explore more formats later, these three are used most frequently. They will make your task easier. Whenever possible, data should be converted into a graph. The rest of this chapter will show you how to construct and use different kinds of graphs.

45 It has been said that a picture is worth a thousand words. Pictures save time in the communication process and help the audience stay alert. They greatly enhance presentations to management.

46

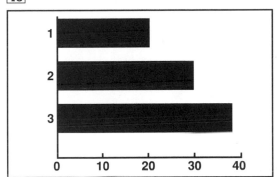

Column or bar graphs are a familiar way to present data.

47

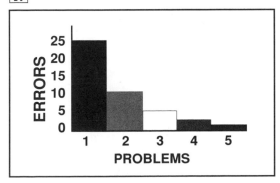

This is a Pareto chart, which is a form of column graph.

A Pareto chart graphically prioritizes information for decision analysis by placing the largest column on the left side of the chart. All other columns are arranged in descending order. The chapter on Pareto analysis explains how to do this.

49

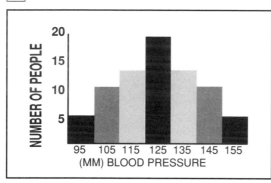

This is another type of column graph called a histogram.

50 You can use a histogram if you take the same measurement on many identical units.

51

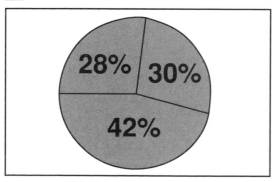

This pie chart depicts the market share of three factories that make the same product.

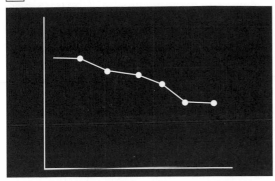

This is an example of a line graph.

STOP THE AV

Have each member draw a line graph using the following data.

NOW, ADVANCE TO FRAME #53. DO NOT START THE AUDIOTAPE YET.

Tell them their graph should look like the graph on the frame. (If any members have trouble with this task, the leader or facilitator should assist them.)

START THE AUDIOTAPE

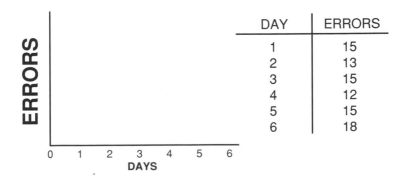

DAY	ERRORS
1	15
2	13
3	15
4	12
5	15
6	18

© 1991 QCI INTERNATIONAL
REPRODUCTION PROHIBITED

143

4-15

DATA-COLLECTION FORMATS
PLUS GRAPHS

53

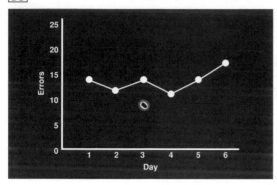

A line graph is frequently used to visually represent data.

54

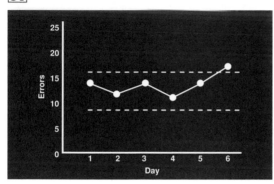

This is the same line graph with control limit lines added. Any time the line breaks out beyond a control limit, it indicates a problem may exist.

55

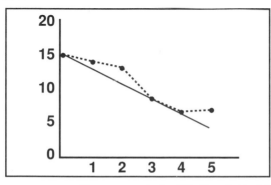

You can establish a target or plan by drawing a heavy solid line from the present level to the final target level. This graph shows the target level of improvement and how long the group expects to take in reaching it. The actual results are posted with the dotted line as they occur.

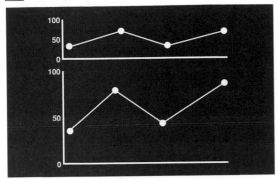

Do not mislead with graphs. Although these graphs do not appear to be similar, they actually display identical information.

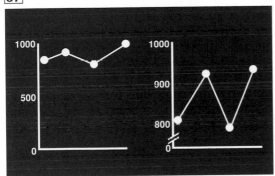

Here's another example of how graphs can mislead. Again, identical information is portrayed, but the viewer's impression may be completely different.

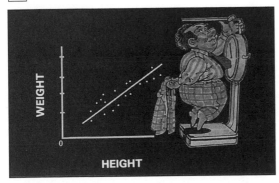

A scatter diagram displays the relationship between two kinds of data. In this example, each plot point represents the height and weight of a different man. When information for a number of men is posted, a pattern is formed.

© 1991 QCI INTERNATIONAL
REPRODUCTION PROHIBITED

145

4-17

DATA-COLLECTION FORMATS
PLUS GRAPHS

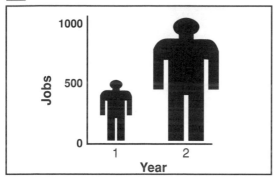

Pictographs employ pictures to add visual punch to a chart. The approach shown here should be avoided, because without explanation, it may lead the viewer to believe the number of jobs increased four-fold, when actually it only doubled.

60

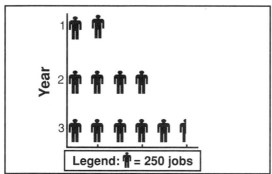

You can convey the same information without danger of misinforming by using this format. The use of a partial symbol is demonstrated during the third year.

61   When using graphs, always add a legend and a title. All team documents should include information identifying who was involved and when it happened.

62   Here's a brief review of what you have learned.

63 Members need data if they are to solve problems. A variety of data-collection techniques helps speed and simplify the process.

64

> ## Ways to Collect Data
> ### 1. Checklists
> ### 2. Drawings
> ### 3. Check Sheets

Some of the more commonly used formats include: (1) checklists, (2) drawings, (3) check sheets.

65 There is a variety of graphs. Team members should practice using them.

66 Graphs can communicate the group's recommendation to management convincingly in a minimum amount of time.

© 1991 QCI INTERNATIONAL
REPRODUCTION PROHIBITED

147
4-19

DATA-COLLECTION FORMATS
PLUS GRAPHS

NOTES

SUMMARY SHEET

Data-Collection Formats Plus Graphs

- Members need data to solve problems.

- Three common formats for collecting data are:

  1. checklists
  2. drawings
  3. check sheets

- A memory hook is a type of checklist.

- Steps in developing a check sheet:

  1. Decide what information to collect.
  2. Decide on the time period to collect data.
  3. Design a form that will help you collect and organize data.
  4. Record data on the form.

- Why use graphs and charts? A picture is worth a thousand words.

- Successful teams develop milestone charts for each project.

- Before designing formats and collecting data, check to see if the desired information has already been collected.

NOTES

WORK SHEET EXERCISES

1. Errors are occurring at an increasing rate in the company mailroom. This is apparent because of a recent rash of complaints. You are not sure of specifics, so you decide to do an analysis.

Facts

On Monday—4 letters lacked complete addresses, 7 lacked the sender's name and address, 2 had insufficient postage, and 5 were not processed.

On Tuesday—2 letters lacked complete addresses, 6 lacked the sender's name and address, and 8 were not processed.

On Wednesday—9 letters lacked the sender's name and address, and 13 were not processed.

On Thursday—3 lacked complete addresses, 4 lacked the sender's name and address, 17 were torn by the postage metering machine, 3 had insufficient postage, and 2 were not processed.

On Friday—3 lacked the sender's name and address, 5 were torn by the postage metering machine, and 11 were delivered to the wrong office within the company.

Assignment

1. Make a check sheet and post the mailroom data on it.

2. Identify at least two important data points or patterns on this check sheet.

© 1991 QCI INTERNATIONAL
REPRODUCTION PROHIBITED

151

4-23

DATA-COLLECTION FORMATS
PLUS GRAPHS

2. Different chart formats can often portray the same information.

Facts

Three crews of equal size are doing identical work. The error quantities for the week are as follows:

Crew A: 20%
Crew B: 50%
Crew C: 30%
‾‾‾‾‾
100%

Assignment

Depict this information using a:

A. Pie chart

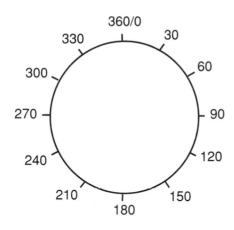

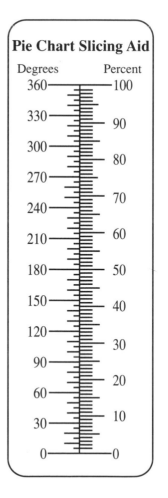

Instructions for Use of Pie Chart Slicing Aid

You've heard the expressions, "Turn 180 degrees" or "Make a 90 degree turn to your left." These expressions come from the concept of a circle having 360 degrees. There's nothing special about the number 360. We could just as easily have chosen to divide a circle into 1,000 parts. The number 360 is the standard number everyone uses today.

On the Pie Chart Slicing Aid, notice that 100% is exactly 360 degrees, 50% is exactly half (180 degrees), and 0% is also 0 degrees.

To use it, simply locate the percentage you are concerned with. In this case, Crew A made 20% of the errors. Look to the left and you can see 20% is approximately equal to 70 degrees (72 to be exact).

Put a dot in the middle of the circle and draw a line from the dot to the point that shows "360/0." Then draw a second line from the dot to where you think 72 degrees is. You'll have to estimate it. Continue for Crews B and C.

B. Bar graph

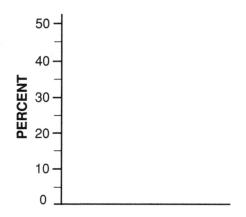

© 1991 QCI INTERNATIONAL
REPRODUCTION PROHIBITED

153

DATA-COLLECTION FORMATS
PLUS GRAPHS

4-25

NOTES

REVIEW QUESTIONS

1. Name three general formats you can use to collect data.

   a. _____

   b. _____

   c. _____

2. Drawings showing the location of defects would be less applicable in a company manufacturing carpeting than in one manufacturing hardware.

   True _____   False _____

3. Both a column graph and a pie graph can portray identical data.

   True _____   False _____

4. The information on several job questionnaires could be transferred to a check sheet to compare applicants' qualifications.

   True _____   False _____

5. Which technique is most likely to follow the use of a check sheet?

   a. Cause-&-effect analysis
   b. Pareto analysis
   c. Brainstorming

6. A check sheet helps ensure:

   a. Time will be saved in collecting data
   b. Data collected will be uniformly arranged
   c. Analysis time will be minimized
   d. All of the above

7. The "5 W's and an H" is an example of a memory hook.

   True _____   False _____

© 1991 QCI INTERNATIONAL
REPRODUCTION PROHIBITED

155

4-27

DATA-COLLECTION FORMATS
PLUS GRAPHS

8. The facilitator is responsible for collecting data needed by the group.

True _____   False _____

9. It is preferable to collect slightly more data than you first estimate you will need.

True _____   False _____

10. Why did you answer question #9 the way you did?

_____

_____

_____

_____

11. Occasionally, information is collected by posting data onto the check sheet as it occurs.

True _____   False _____

ANSWERS TO WORK SHEET EXERCISES

1. The following check sheet was constructed from information contained in the exercise. Important data points or patterns have been circled and explanatory notes are included.

CHECK SHEET

Almost always

Error	Mon.	Tue.	Wed.	Thur.	Fri.	Total
Lacked Complete Address	////	//		///		9
Omitted Sender's Name	TTHL //	TTHL /	THL ////	////	///	29
Insufficient Postage	//			///		5
Not Processed	THL	THL ///	THL THL ///	//		28
Torn by Metering Machine				THL THL THL //	THL	22
Delivered to Wrong Office					THL iHLI	11
Total	18	16	22	29	19	104

Got better   Heavy on Thur.   Only on Fri.

2. A. Pie Chart

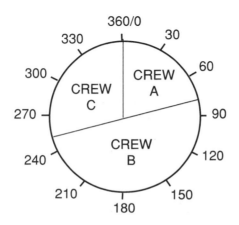

© 1991 QCI INTERNATIONAL
REPRODUCTION PROHIBITED

157

4-29

DATA-COLLECTION FORMATS
PLUS GRAPHS

B. Bar graph

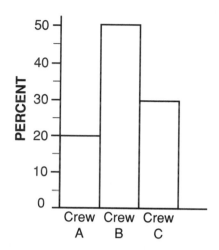

ANSWERS TO REVIEW QUESTIONS

1. a. Check sheets
   b. Checklists
   c. Drawings showing the location of defects

2. False

3. True

4. True

5. b. Pareto analysis

6. d. All of the above

7. True

8. False

9. True

10. Original estimates may prove inadequate. By collecting more data than you first estimate is necessary, the excess data may save you the trouble of repeating the data-collection exercise.

11. True

NOTES

DECISION ANALYSIS USING PARETO

INTERNATIONAL
Red Bluff, CA 96080

MEETING NOTES

Decision Analysis Using Pareto

Prior to Meeting

- Review pages 165 through 195 of this chapter.

- Confer with facilitator.

- Post final agenda. A suggested agenda follows:

AGENDA
(Date)

Opening activities
– Minutes.
– Status of action items.
– Review last training topic.
– Review milestone chart.

Today's Training Topic
– Review objectives.
– Present AV.

Discussion
– Review summary sheet.
– Discuss work sheet/review questions.

Closing Items
– Review action items.
– Set next meeting's agenda.

During Meeting

Prior to AV

- Welcome members and introduce guests.

- Review the posted agenda for today's meeting.

- Have the minutes of the last meeting read and approved.

- Ask for status report on any action items from previous meeting.

- Review and discuss the material on "Data-Collection Formats Plus Graphs." Discuss any completed work sheet exercises or redo some review questions if helpful.

- Introduce "Decision Analysis Using Pareto." Review objectives listed on page 165. You might have several members read them aloud.

During AV

- Present the AV module, stopping where the manual suggests and elsewhere if helpful.

After AV

- Get maximum involvement in a discussion of the material. Be sure to include a discussion of the summary sheet.

- Have the group answer and discuss some or all of the work sheet exercises and review questions at the end of this chapter.

- Review the objectives again. Ask members if they feel the objectives were met.

- Update milestone chart.

- Get member input in setting the agenda for the next meeting.

- Ask for volunteers to do action items.

- Suggest members read the chapter "Basic Cause-&-Effect Analysis" before the next meeting.

- Announce the date, time and place of the next meeting.

- Thank attendees for their attention and cooperation.

- Adjourn the meeting.

After Meeting

- Meet with your facilitator to discuss the meeting.

- Follow up to make sure the minutes are completed and distributed.

- If possible, put the agenda for the next meeting in a place easily seen by members.

NOTES

Decision Analysis Using Pareto

OBJECTIVES

- To understand how Pareto analysis can be used as a decision-making tool.

- To learn the steps involved in constructing a Pareto chart.

- To learn how to construct and use a cumulative line.

- To learn where and how to use weighting factors in doing a Pareto analysis.

- To learn how to stratify data.

---

[1]   (Graphic—can be substituted with organization logo)

[2]   (Credits)

DECISION ANALYSIS USING PARETO

Teams make decisions on a variety of subjects. One decision-analysis tool used by teams is the Pareto chart.

4   Decisions are often difficult to make. Pareto charts make the process easier by organizing data so that comparisons can be made based on facts.

5   Vilfredo Pareto, a 19th century European scholar, pointed out that 95 percent of the wealth was controlled by only 5 percent of the people.

6	Today, 80 percent of sales often are made by 20 percent of the sales force.

7	Ninety percent of office errors may be made by 10 percent of the employees.

8	Eighty percent of the scrap may be generated by 20 percent of the work force.

STOP THE AV

Ask: Can anyone think of situations where the 80-20, 90-10 rule might apply?

Some situations:

- Eighty percent of charitable contributions are made by 20 percent of the people.

- Ninety percent of the crimes are committed by 10 percent of the population.

- Eighty percent of the customer complaints are made by 20 percent of the customers.

Comment: The ratio is not always exactly 80-20 or 90-10. For example, 90 percent of the crimes might be committed by 8 percent of the population.

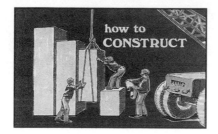

9

There are several steps in constructing a Pareto chart.

10 **Step 1.** Decide on the type of data you will gather. Careful consideration at this time will better ensure a minimum of trouble later.

11 **Step 2.** Determine the time period when data is to be collected. Although you may need only a few hours, some projects require days or even months.

12 **Step 3.** Design a form, usually a check sheet, you can use to collect the necessary data. Ideally, it should be general enough to allow information to be arranged in a variety of ways in case the first effort fails.

13

Step 4. Record the data on the check sheet. Let's look at an example from an accounting department.

14

CHECK SHEET

JUNE

ERROR	1	2	3	4	TOTAL
ADDITION	𝙸𝙷𝙻	𝙸𝙷𝙻 ////	𝙸𝙷𝙻 /	𝙸𝙷𝙻 //	27
MULTIPLICATION	𝙸𝙷𝙻 𝙸𝙷𝙻 𝙸𝙷𝙻 ////	𝙸𝙷𝙻 𝙸𝙷𝙻 𝙸𝙷𝙻 𝙸𝙷𝙻 //	𝙸𝙷𝙻 𝙸𝙷𝙻 ////	𝙸𝙷𝙻 𝙸𝙷𝙻 𝙸𝙷𝙻	70
OMISSION	///	𝙸𝙷𝙻 /	//	/	12
ROUTING	//		/	///	6
TYPING	𝙸𝙷𝙻 /	𝙸𝙷𝙻	𝙸𝙷𝙻 //	𝙸𝙷𝙻 //	25
TOTAL	35	42	30	33	140

This is the completed check sheet. The total of all the errors equals 140.

STOP THE AV

Comment: Let's pause for a few moments to give members time to study this check sheet.

Step 5. Construct Pareto charts using the data on the check sheet.

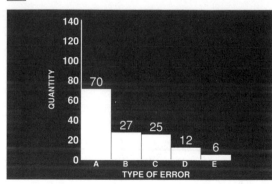

This Pareto chart is constructed from the previous check sheet. Notice the columns are arranged in descending order from left to right.

17   Suppose all the columns were arranged in one single tall stack.

18

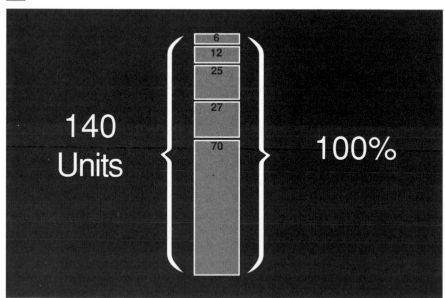

It would form a column 140 units high, equal to 100 percent. Remember, the 140 units refers to the total of 140 errors recorded on the check sheet.

19 **Step 6.** Construct the cumulative line. This step is optional. Members know the stack reaches a height equal to 140 units, or 100 percent.

20

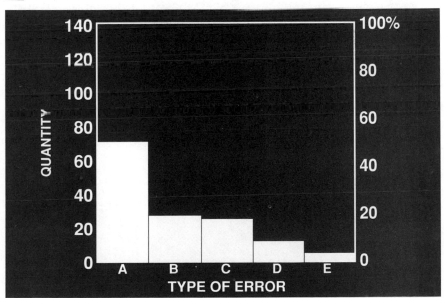

Set up a percentage scale on the right-hand side that goes from 0 to 100 percent. In our example, 140 equals 100 percent of the errors.

DECISION ANALYSIS
USING PARETO

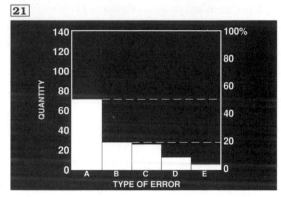

21

By itself, the right-hand percentage scale can be used to quickly estimate the percentage of the total each individual column represents. In this example, you can estimate the first column is 50 percent of the errors, the second column is 19 percent of the errors and so on.

22

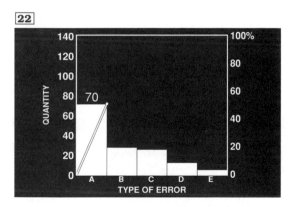

To construct a cumulative line, start at 0 and draw a line to the top right-hand corner of the first column. It is now at the 70 level.

23

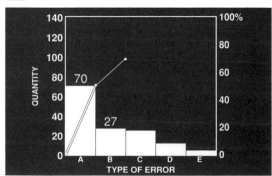

Continue the cumulative line to a point 27 units higher (27 + 70 = 97) and directly above the right-hand edge of the second column.

24 Do the same for the next column of 25 units.

25 Then extend the line for the column of 12 units.

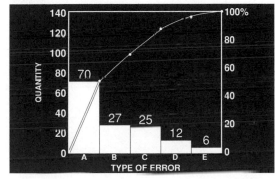

When the cumulative line is drawn for the last column of six units, it should reach the 100 percent level as in the percentage scale on the right side.

STOP THE AV

Ask: Does anyone have any questions on how to construct the cumulative line?

---

*DECISION ANALYSIS
USING PARETO*

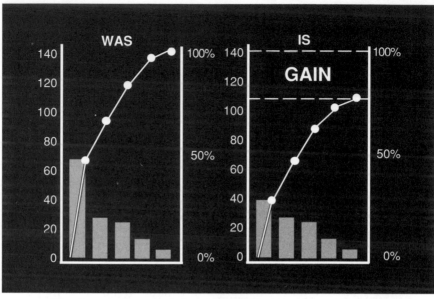

27

The foremost use of the cumulative line is to visually compare before-and-after situations.

STOP THE AV

Comment: Let's pause for a few moments to give members time to study these Pareto Charts.

28

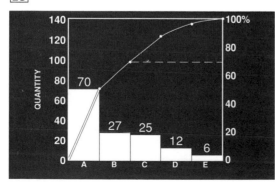

Cumulative lines can be used to determine the percentage of the total of several columns. In this example, you can estimate the first two columns represent 70 percent of the errors.

DECISION ANALYSIS
USING PARETO

174

5-10

© *1991 QCI INTERNATIONAL*
REPRODUCTION PROHIBITED

29

This is another variation on how to present a before-and-after comparison. The columns of the two Pareto charts are simply stacked.

30

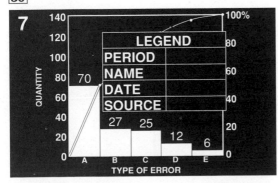

Step 7. Add a legend so that anyone can understand the meaning of the chart.

© 1991 QCI INTERNATIONAL
REPRODUCTION PROHIBITED

175

5-11

DECISION ANALYSIS
USING PARETO

31 So far, Pareto charts based on errors have been discussed. The cost of those errors is usually a more important consideration.

32

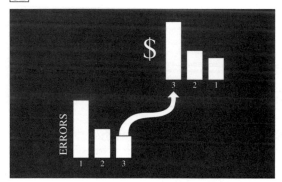

Sometimes, when the columns shown by errors are converted to money, the order of importance is changed.

33 To do this, you will need to use weighting factors. Weighting factors can be based on dollars, urgency, customer importance, etc. Their use helps to correctly prioritize the situation.

34

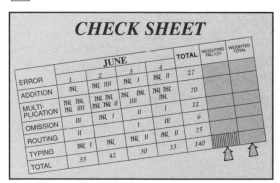

For example, you may feel some types of errors are more important than others. Therefore, you can add two columns to the right.

CHECK SHEET

	JUNE 1	2	3	4	TOTAL	WEIGHTING FACTOR	WEIGHTED TOTAL
ERROR	1	꧑ IIII	꧑ I	꧑ II	27	1	
ADDITION	꧑	꧑ IIII	꧑ ꧑ IIII	꧑ ꧑ ꧑	70	1	
MULTI-PLICATION	꧑ ꧑ ꧑ IIII	꧑ ꧑ ꧑ ꧑ II		I	12	2	
OMISSION	III	꧑ I	II	III	6	2	
ROUTING	II		I	III	25	3	
TYPING	꧑ I	꧑	꧑ II	꧑ II	140		
TOTAL	35	42	30	33	140		

In the first new column, you place the weighting factor. The more importance attached, the greater the weighting factor. In a situation where you would wish to weight the data by money, you could show the cost of each error. In our simple example here, the errors cost one, two or three dollars, depending on which error you are talking about.

*DECISION ANALYSIS
USING PARETO*

CHECK SHEET

ERROR	JUNE 1	2	3	4	TOTAL	WEIGHTING FACTOR	WEIGHTED TOTAL
ADDITION	卌	卌 IIII	卌 I	卌 II	27	1	27
MULTIPLICATION	卌 卌 卌 IIII	卌 卌 卌 卌 II	卌 卌 IIII	卌 卌 卌	70	1	70
OMISSION	III	卌 I	II	I	12	2	24
ROUTING	II		I	III	6	2	12
TYPING	卌 I	卌	卌 II	卌 II	25	3	75
TOTAL	35	42	30	33	140		208

Each error category is multiplied by the weighting factor to get the new weighted total. Often, this technique causes a change in the order of priorities. In this instance, the main problem was changed from multiplication to typing.

[37] Why are weighting factors used? For example, no one wants an unhappy customer. So find out what your customers' priorities are and respond accordingly.

[38] You might decide to use weighting factors because of urgency. Two examples might be legal considerations or government regulations.

39

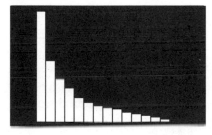

Occasionally, a Pareto chart may contain a large number of columns.

40

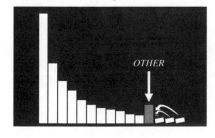

Often, trivial columns are lumped together under one column titled "Other." You should use caution here. Do not bury and overlook a small, but significant, column in this way. For example, the smallest column may be the one that costs the most if you converted the Pareto chart to dollars.

DECISION ANALYSIS
USING PARETO

41

A technique called stratification can help. It separates or rearranges data so you can find more meaningful ways to present it. Here you see the water faucet pulled apart to understand more about it.

42

A Pareto chart arranged by errors could take on this appearance. No category stands out. Perhaps it should be arranged by the shifts that produced the errors.

43

Grouping by shift is no improvement. Still no column stands out. Arranging the chart by the machine that produced the errors might be better.

44

Organizing the chart by machine proves successful. One column clearly stands out to indicate that machine No. 3 is the source of the problem. At this point, you can immediately do a second Pareto chart dealing with errors on machine No. 3 only.

45 Let's look at another example of stratification.

46 Imagine that some electro-mechanical units are being rejected for a variety of reasons. An investigation leads to the creation of two related Pareto charts.

47

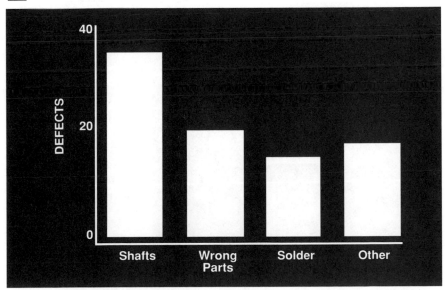

This first Pareto chart shows the shafts are the biggest reasons for rejection of the units.

© 1991 QCI INTERNATIONAL
REPRODUCTION PROHIBITED

181

5-17

DECISION ANALYSIS
USING PARETO

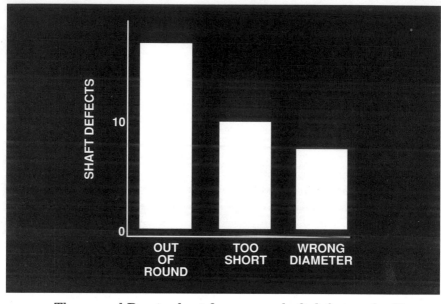

48

The second Pareto chart focuses on shaft defects only. The chart shows that most shafts are out-of-round. There are instances when three, four or more successive Pareto diagrams might be required. Doing so might provide valuable new insight.

49

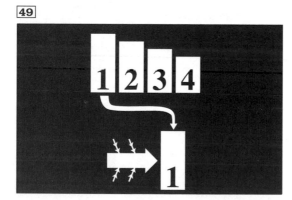

After the Pareto chart identifies the major problem, then what? That No. 1 problem is then subjected to cause-&-effect analysis to find the true cause.

50   There are many applications for Pareto analysis.

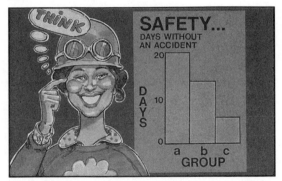

For example, the number of safety days without an accident for each work group can be shown on a Pareto chart.

52

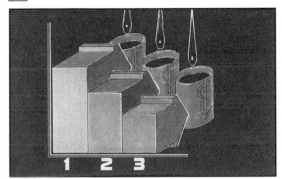

Or, oil well production can be illustrated on a Pareto chart.

53

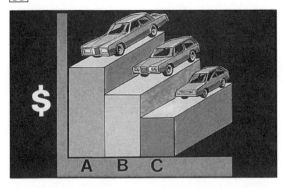

Some automobiles hold their value better than others, as this chart suggests.

54 Pareto charts can be posted in the work area to keep employees informed of progress on various projects, products and services.

55 Presentations to management are more effective when members display visual aids such as Pareto charts.

56 In conclusion, Pareto charts can help make decisions on a variety of topics.

SUMMARY SHEET

Pareto Chart Construction

1. Decide on the type of data you will gather.

2. Determine the time period.

3. Design a check sheet.

4. Record data on the check sheet.

5. Construct the Pareto chart.

6. Construct the cumulative line (optional).

7. Add a legend.

Other Key Points

1. A cumulative line is used mainly for before-and-after comparisons.

2. A cumulative line is optional.

3. A Pareto chart can provide useful information even if one column does not boldly stand out.

4. Converting errors or defects to dollars can be very helpful.

NOTES

WORK SHEET EXERCISES

1. Pareto charts help us visualize alternatives. You can construct them using information gathered on a check sheet.

   Assignment

   (1) Using the check sheet below, construct a Pareto chart.

   (2) Add in the cumulative line.

CHECK SHEET

	Mon.	Tue.	Wed.	Thur.	Fri.	Total
Lacked Complete Address	I I I I	I I		I I I		9
Omitted Sender's Name	⊓⊤⊥⊣ I I	⊓⊤⊥⊣ I	⊓⊤⊥⊣ I I I I	I I I I	I I I	2 9
Insufficient Postage	I I			I I I		5
Not Processed	⊓⊤⊥⊣	⊓⊤⊥⊣ I I I	⊓⊤⊥⊣ ⊓⊤⊥⊣ I I I	I I		2 8
Torn by Metering Machine				⊓⊤⊥ I ⊓⊤⊥⊣ I I	⊓⊤⊥ I I ⊓⊤⊥ I I	2 2
Delivered to Wrong Office					⊓⊤⊥⊣ ⊓⊤⊥⊣ I	1 1
Total	1 8	1 6	2 2	2 9	1 9	1 0 4

DECISION ANALYSIS
USING PARETO

2. Sometimes, in doing decision analysis, you can add weighting factors to put things in the correct order.

Facts

Two types of errors are considered more significant than others. Therefore, they are weighted as follows:

Error	Weight
• Incomplete address	2
• Delivered to wrong party	3
• All other errors	1

Assignment

(1) Add a weighting column to the check sheet used in question #1. Add another column to the right of it titled "Weighted Total."

(2) Construct another Pareto chart based on this new information.

(3) Draw in the cumulative line.

REVIEW QUESTIONS

1. Every Pareto chart must have a column labeled "other" to reduce the number of minor columns.

   True _____   False _____

2. Theoretically, the maximum number of columns a Pareto chart can have is:

   a. six
   b. ten
   c. no limit

3. The minimum number of columns a Pareto chart can have is:

   a. two
   b. three
   c. four

4. The cumulative line can be used to estimate the percentage of the total each column represents.

   True _____   False _____

5. A cumulative line makes before-and-after comparisons easier to visualize.

   True _____   False _____

6. Normally, what technique is used before constructing a Pareto chart?

   a. Cumulative line
   b. Check sheet
   c. Cause-&-effect analysis

7. Normally, what technique follows the Pareto chart?

   a. Cause-&-effect analysis
   b. Brainstorming
   c. Check sheet

© 1991 QCI INTERNATIONAL
REPRODUCTION PROHIBITED

189

5-25

DECISION ANALYSIS
USING PARETO

8. Using a cumulative line is:

   a. mandatory
   b. recommended for some applications

9. The Pareto chart columns may be arranged in descending order from either left to right or vice versa.

   True _____   False _____

10. It may be advantageous to arrange the columns of a Pareto chart by dollar amounts as well as by quantity of defects.

   True _____   False _____

11. Should Pareto chart columns ever be arranged by degree of urgency?

   Yes _____   No _____

12. Sometimes the results of one Pareto chart can trigger a second Pareto chart.

   True _____   False _____

ANSWER TO WORK SHEET
EXERCISE 1

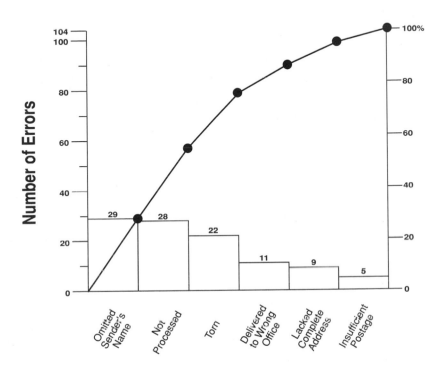

© 1991 QCI INTERNATIONAL
REPRODUCTION PROHIBITED

191

5-27

DECISION ANALYSIS
USING PARETO

ANSWER TO WORK SHEET
EXERCISE 2

CHECK SHEET

	Mon.	Tue.	Wed.	Thur.	Fri.	Total	Weight	Weighted Total
Lacked Complete Address	I I I	I I		I I I		9	2	18
Omitted Sender's Name	⊬⊬⊔ I I	⊬⊬⊔ I	⊬⊬⊔ I I I I	I I I I	I I I	29	1	29
Insufficient Postage	I I			I I I		5	1	5
Not Processed	⊬⊬⊔	⊬⊬⊔ I I I	⊬⊬⊔ ⊬⊬⊔ I I I	I I		28	1	28
Torn by Metering Machine				⊬⊬⊔ ⊬⊬⊔ ⊬⊬⊔ I I	⊬⊬⊔	22	1	22
Delivered to Wrong Office					⊬⊬⊔ ⊬⊬⊔ I	11	3	33
Total	18	16	22	29	19	104		135

DECISION ANALYSIS
USING PARETO

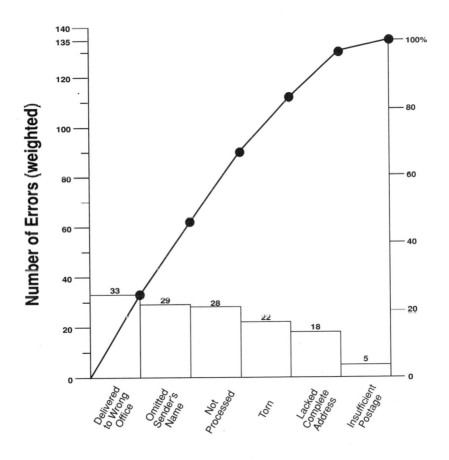

© 1991 QCI INTERNATIONAL
REPRODUCTION PROHIBITED

193

5-29

DECISION ANALYSIS
USING PARETO

NOTES

ANSWERS TO REVIEW QUESTIONS

1. False

2. c. no limit

3. a. two

4. True

5. True

6. b. Check sheet

7. a. Cause-&-effect analysis

8. b. recommended for some applications

9. False. By definition, a Pareto chart should show columns descending from left to right.

10. True

11. Yes

12. True

© 1991 QCI INTERNATIONAL
REPRODUCTION PROHIBITED

195

5-31

DECISION ANALYSIS
USING PARETO

NOTES

BASIC
CAUSE-&-EFFECT
ANALYSIS

INTERNATIONAL
Red Bluff, CA 96080

MEETING NOTES

Basic Cause-&-Effect Analysis

Prior to Meeting

- Review pages 201 through 227 of this chapter.

- Confer with facilitator.

- Post final agenda. A suggested agenda follows:

AGENDA
(Date)

Opening Activities
– Minutes.
– Status of action items.
– Review last training topic.
– Review milestone chart.

Today's Training Topic
– Review objectives.
– Present AV.

Discussion
– Review summary sheet.
– Discuss work sheet/review questions.

Closing Items
– Review action items.
– Set next meeting's agenda.

During Meeting

Prior to AV

* Welcome members and introduce guests.

* Review the posted agenda for today's meeting.

* Have the minutes of the last meeting read and approved.

* Ask for status report on any action items from previous meeting.

* Review and discuss the material on "Decision Analysis Using Pareto." Discuss the work sheet. Ask a few of the review questions to review the lesson quickly.

* Introduce "Basic Cause-&-Effect Analysis." Basic cause-&-effect analysis, one of the most powerful techniques teams can use, provides a way to group ideas. This organized system helps members keep up with the data needed to solve problems. Groups that regularly practice this technique quickly become skilled at it. Help your group develop by including a case example in this training session.

    LEADER NOTE: Learning occurs through reinforcement. Your team should do two or three basic cause-&-effect diagrams before they actually start one for a project.

* Review objectives listed on page 201.

During AV

* Present the AV module, stopping where the manual suggests and elsewhere if helpful.

After AV

- Demonstration:

  The group will enjoy the following exercise. Ask members to take off their wristwatches without looking at them. Have them put the watches out of sight. Each member should draw a sketch of the face of their watch. They should include as much detail as possible.

  Remind the group of the importance of observing details while solving problems. The mind tends to filter out everything that is commonplace, remembering only what has changed. In problem solving, you frequently need to know some of that information your mind has blotted out. For example, suppose you had to identify your watch. Do you really know what it looks like?

  Ask members to compare their watches with their sketches. Ask questions like:

  "Are the hours indicated by numbers or marks?"
  "Are there 12 numbers?"
  "What color is the face?"
  "Is there a second hand?"
  "What is written on the face?"

  A surprising number of people will miss one or more of these questions.

  Remind the group that good problem solving requires attention to detail and seeing things they may now overlook.

- Get maximum involvement in a discussion of the material. Be sure to include a discussion of the summary sheet.

- Have the group answer and discuss some or all of the work sheet exercises and review questions at the end of this chapter.

- Review the objectives again. Ask members if they feel the objectives were met.

- Update milestone chart.

- Get member input in setting the agenda for the next meeting.

- Ask for volunteers to do action items.

- Suggest members read the chapter "Process Cause-&-Effect Analysis" before the next meeting.

- Announce the date, time and place of the next meeting.

- Thank attendees for their attention and cooperation.

- Adjourn the meeting.

After Meeting

- Meet with your facilitator to discuss the meeting.

- Follow up to make sure the minutes are completed and distributed.

- If possible, post the agenda for the next meeting in a place easily seen by members.

Basic Cause-&-Effect Analysis

OBJECTIVES

- To understand the uses of basic cause-&-effect analysis.

- To be able to demonstrate the steps involved in doing basic cause-&-effect analysis.

- To be able to use basic cause-&-effect analysis to find causes of effects, whether they are bad or good.

---

1   (Graphic—can be substituted with organization logo)

2   (Credits)

BASIC CAUSE-&-EFFECT ANALYSIS

The primary purpose of basic cause-&-effect analysis is to help the group solve problems.

4   The problem is the effect, written in the box to the right. The possible causes are written in the area to the left.

5

One look at a completed cause-&-effect analysis shows why it is often called a fishbone diagram.

6   Too often the boss excludes other employees and attempts to solve all problems.

7   Sometimes the boss asks staff people to solve problems.

8   What about getting the employees who do the work involved?

9

No one goes to a barber to get relief from a toothache. It makes sense to take problems to the experts. In any organization, the expert at a job is the person actually doing it.

10   Members select a problem to analyze from within their area of responsibility. Problem selection is often based on Pareto analysis results.

BASIC CAUSE-&-EFFECT ANALYSIS

During cause-&-effect analysis, a person (either a member or the leader) writes the ideas on the chart so everyone can see them and to create a permanent record. Groups should use a large piece of paper or an overhead projector. They should avoid using note pads or erasable boards.

Basic cause-&-effect analysis involves six steps. **Step 1.** State the effect. In this case, the effect is a problem, a TV set that doesn't work properly. Members should define the problem as specifically as possible.

13 For example, if members know the sound on the TV doesn't work, they should include this information in the problem definition. This knowledge will ensure members can more accurately pinpoint possible causes. They also will save time in solving the problem.

14 Members should refrain from trying to solve problems in areas where they have no expertise.

STOP THE AV

Discuss the concept of the "expert" with the group.

Ask: In what areas are you the expert?
Answers include the work that I perform, the way to operate equipment in my area, and everything that occurs in my area while I do my job.

Ask: In what areas are you not the expert?
Answers include how work is done in other areas, how that operator performs his/her part of the job, and why things are done the way they are in "that other" department.

15

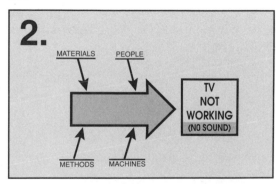

Step 2. Identify the major cause groups. Any number of such groups is possible. Members usually identify three or four groups. Start out with the three M's and a P (materials, methods, machines and people).

BASIC CAUSE-&-EFFECT
ANALYSIS

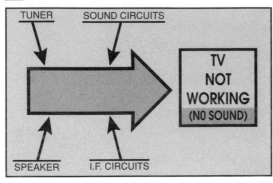

16

As your group becomes more experienced, consider choosing major cause groups that fit the problem better.

17 **Step 3.** Involve all members in a brainstorming session to identify possible causes.

18 The leader should review the rules of brainstorming prior to starting this session.

19 Each member is asked, in rotation, for ideas. This continues until all ideas are exhausted.

20 A member may have several ideas but can offer only one per turn.

21   When members have no idea, they simply say "Pass."

22   No idea should be treated as stupid. Don't evaluate ideas during brainstorming.

23   Members usually can come up with many ideas when they think in terms of the five W's and one H (what, why, when, where, who and how).

24

Exaggeration is encouraged.

25   When the rules have been explained, the team can begin brainstorming.

BASIC CAUSE-&-EFFECT
ANALYSIS

26 The process is speeded up substantially when a member writes the ideas on the chart as they are given.

27 Members should indicate under which heading they want their idea included. For example, in the case of the TV sound not working, a member might say, "Under materials write 'speaker.'"

28

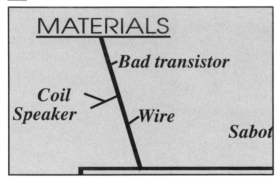

Occasionally, a cause can be added as a branch extending from a cause already on the chart. This cause could be stated as, "Under materials, as a branch from 'speaker,' put 'coil.'"

29

During the brainstorming step, some members tend to jump ahead and state solutions rather than possible causes. It is too early to assume the true cause has been identified. For the problem of bad-tasting coffee, it would be wrong to prematurely say, "Buy a new pot."

30 The leader should clarify the member was stating a solution. The member could then restate his or her idea as "Defective coffee pot."

31 The cause-&-effect diagram should show similar ideas grouped together in clumps. This makes the cause easier to analyze.

32 Brainstorming continues until everyone passes.

33

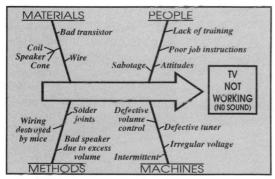

The cause-&-effect diagram may look like this at that time.

34

Step 4. Consider the ideas collected during brainstorming and select the most likely causes.

BASIC CAUSE-&-EFFECT
ANALYSIS

| 35 | Identifying the most likely causes can be a time-consuming process involving a long discussion of each cause. |

| 36 | Or the process can be speeded up by allowing members to vote for each cause they believe to be important. |

| 37 |

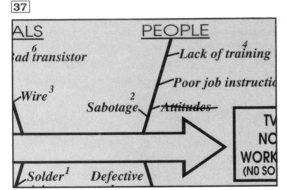

The leader tells members they may vote for as many causes as they wish. The leader begins by pointing to one of the causes and asking, for example, "How many think 'Lack of training' is one of the main causes of our problem?" In this case, four people voted for it, and "4" is recorded on the diagram. This procedure continues until all causes have been voted on. When a cause gets no votes, simply draw a line through it.

| 38 | Next, causes with the highest number of votes are circled. Usually, the group circles between two and six, but there is no set number. |

| 39 | In our example, the three causes receiving the highest number of votes were circled. |

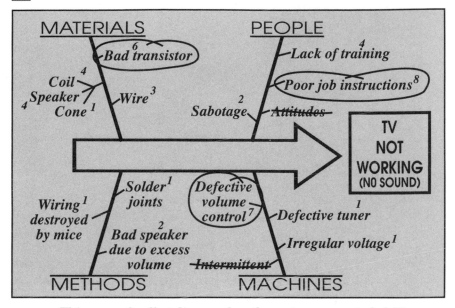

This cause-&-effect diagram has the major causes circled. Now the members can focus on just a few causes—much less confusing!

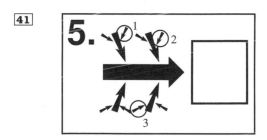

Step 5. Rank the most probable causes in order of importance.

To do this, the group looks only at those causes that have been circled. Each is discussed in detail prior to any voting.

© 1991 QCI INTERNATIONAL
REPRODUCTION PROHIBITED

211

6-11

BASIC CAUSE-&-EFFECT
ANALYSIS

43

Look For

CHANGES

When considering each circled cause, members should look for something that has changed. Few things serve as better clues.

44   They should look for things that are different. If a person's weight increases or decreases unexpectedly, it might be related to changes in diet or exercise patterns.

45   Police look for patterns that help them identify criminals. "M.O." means method of operation. Patterns are useful tools in any field of problem analysis.

46

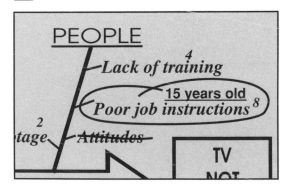

PEOPLE

—Lack of training ⁴

15 years old
Poor job instructions ⁸

²
tage —Attitudes

TV
NOT

Members should call out additional information such as dates, sizes and number of occurrences. This information should be written on the diagram. Write this data in a different color or underline it to make it stand out.

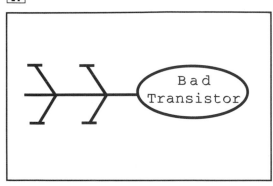

If the group suspects a circled cause is merely a "surface" cause instead of a "root" cause, members can do a special analysis with the circled cause as the effect. The same procedure may have to be repeated as the team pursues the root cause to deeper and deeper levels. Normally, this special approach is unnecessary. But if the group feels they need to do this to arrive at the root cause, they should of course do it.

48 After members have completed evaluation, the final round of voting begins. The number of votes is written beside each major cause. Normally, each member gets only one vote.

49

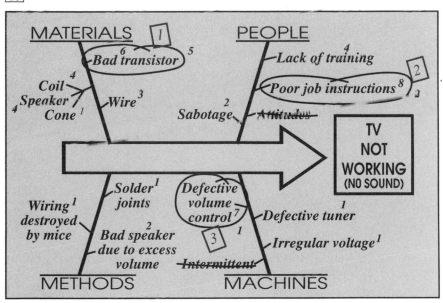

Finally, the priority ranking is added to each of the major causes.

50   In the voting process, do members simply vote, or can they first discuss the causes? Discussion should be encouraged. This is the ideal time to collect information about the causes. All pros, cons and other data should be reported at this time.

51   Would the group ever consider a cause that had not been selected as one of the most likely causes? Certainly. If all circled causes are eliminated, and the problem still exists, the group must look at other possibilities.

STOP THE AV

Ask: In what ways does voting assist in analyzing a problem?

Answers: 1. It speeds up the process.
          2. Everyone is involved.

Comment: Remember, discussion to evaluate pros and cons is acceptable at any time during voting.

---

52   **Step 6.** Test the one most-likely cause in an attempt to verify it. This step might be easy in the case of most TV repairs, or it might be difficult and time-consuming, but it must be done. In cause-&-effect analysis, verification is mandatory.

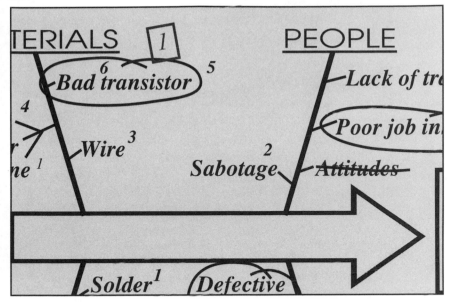

The cause with the highest vote has been labeled #1. The group will attempt to verify this cause first. However, some problems have more than one true cause. The members may test several possible causes in an attempt to verify them.

54 Brainstorming can be helpful at this time. Members should suggest how to verify a given cause. They usually suggest a number of common-sense ways to do it. They should prioritize their ideas and actually test the most likely cause or causes.

55 Airplane manufacturers keep down the cost of verifying by using models. Whatever the team members select as a verification test, it should be tried to see if it supports their conclusions.

*BASIC CAUSE-&-EFFECT
ANALYSIS*

56

Recommended Solutions

After the true cause has been verified, there is an important follow-up to the cause-&-effect analysis: A solution must be found.

57

Cause-&-effect analysis helps members discover and verify the true cause of the problem. Then the group can identify possible solutions.

58

Member involvement is encouraged in identifying ways to correct the problem—another excellent opportunity to use the brainstorming technique. Members usually will suggest a variety of ways to solve the problem.

59

Members discuss the pros and cons of the top alternatives to achieve a consensus. Then they collect data concerning cost and benefits of the top vote-getters. It may be a choice between "Repair" or "Replace."

|60| The recommended solution becomes part of the presentation to management.

|61|  Cause-&-effect analysis is usually employed to solve problems. However, a couple of other applications should be considered.

|62| Occasionally, something unexpectedly takes a turn for the better. Maybe the coffee suddenly starts tasting great. Unless the reason for this is discovered, it may go back to its former characteristics just as suddenly. Cause-&-effect analysis could be used to find the cause of this good effect.

|63| You may find the cause-&-effect diagram an excellent teaching device. The effect might be, for example, "Doing a good job." The brainstorming session would focus on those things that cause the job to be done right.

|64| There are some items to remember when using cause-&-effect analysis.

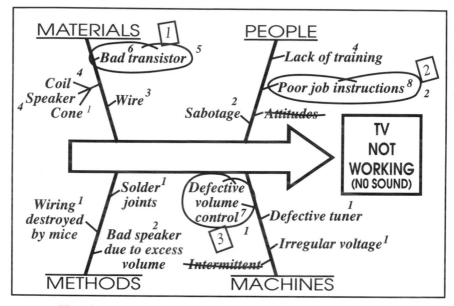

Use the original cause-&-effect diagram when doing the presentation to management. Its realism carries more impact than a diagram that has been neatly redone.

66   The diagram is not finished until a legend has been added. The legend should contain such things as the date, the group name and the subject of the analysis.

BASIC CAUSE-&-EFFECT
ANALYSIS

218

6-18

© 1991 QCI INTERNATIONAL
REPRODUCTION PROHIBITED

SUMMARY SHEET

- Steps in Basic Cause-&-Effect Analysis:

  1. State the effect. Write it in the block on the right side of the cause-&-effect diagram.

  2. Identify the major cause groups. Write them at the ends of the branches from the horizontal centerline. The 3 M's and a P (materials, methods, machines and people) are examples of major cause groups.

  3. Brainstorm for possible causes. In this brainstorming session, the person suggesting the idea should tell the writer where to place the idea on the cause-&-effect diagram.

  4. Select the most likely causes by voting for them. Members may vote for as many causes as they wish during the first round of voting.

  5. Rank the most likely causes through a final round of voting, putting them into the order in which they should be evaluated. Before this final round of voting, gather as much information as possible about the most likely causes. Write the information on the diagram. Normally, in the final round of voting, each member may vote for only one cause.

  6. Test to verify that the selected causes are the true causes.

*BASIC CAUSE-&-EFFECT
ANALYSIS*

- Examples of verification:

Effect:	Flat tire.
Possible cause:	The tire was punctured.
Verification:	Inspect the tire for nails or punctures; then inflate the tire and test its ability to hold pressure.

Effect:	No light from lamp.
Possible cause:	Bulb is burned out.
Verification:	Replace bulb with a bulb that is known to be good.

Effect:	Car overheats.
Possible cause:	No coolant.
Verification:	Check coolant level and fill as needed; then run engine to re-test for overheating.

- Follow-up step—recommended solutions:

After the true cause has been found, the group should develop and test possible solutions. Brainstorming is one way to develop possible solutions. Each possible solution must be tested before it can be put into place.

WORK SHEET EXERCISE

Imagine you lived in central Texas during 1990 in a home with a heat pump. The heat costs for your home went from under $200 per month to $300 in January, then to $500 in February.

Do a basic cause-&-effect analysis on this problem. Follow the steps described on the summary sheet.

*BASIC CAUSE-&-EFFECT
ANALYSIS*

NOTES

REVIEW QUESTIONS

1. The problem to be analyzed should be kept somewhat general in scope to encourage the group to suggest a broad range of possible causes.

   True _____   False _____

2. Just before the brainstorming step of basic cause-and-effect, the rules of brainstorming should be reviewed only when visitors are present.

   True _____   False _____

3. Name the "3 M's and a P."

   _____

   _____

   _____

   _____

4. If suggested causes do not seem to relate to the problem, it is best not to list them.

   True _____   False _____

5. Cause-&-effect analysis must always be led by the leader.

   True _____   False _____

6. During the step where causes are evaluated, how many causes should be circled?

   a. One
   b. Three
   c. No limit

© 1991 QCI INTERNATIONAL
REPRODUCTION PROHIBITED

223

6-23

BASIC CAUSE-&-EFFECT
ANALYSIS

7. What types of clues should the team look for when seeking the most likely causes? Several answers may apply.

   a. Changes
   b. Differences
   c. Recurring patterns
   d. Causes suggested by visiting staff personnel
   e. Causes that generate the most discussion

8. When can discussion of the suggested causes take place?

   a. During brainstorming
   b. During voting to determine the most likely causes
   c. During verification

9. The verification step in cause-&-effect analysis is:

   a. Mandatory
   b. Recommended for some applications
   c. Seldom used

10. Normally, what technique is used just before cause-&-effect analysis?

    a. Brainstorming
    b. Check sheet
    c. Pareto analysis

11. In order of preference, cause-&-effect analysis should be done on a:

    Blackboard   ____
    Note pad   ____
    Large sheet of paper ____
    Overhead projector   ____

ANSWER TO WORK SHEET EXERCISE

Obviously, this problem has many possible causes. Here's one example of what the diagram might look like after the brainstorming step has been completed.

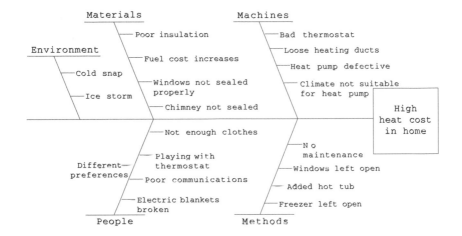

To determine the true cause, you would need to have actually experienced the situation and been able to run a real verification test.

In an actual case upon which this exercise is based, the principal cause related to the fact that the main heating duct had come loose. When it was replaced, heat costs returned to normal levels.

BASIC CAUSE-&-EFFECT ANALYSIS

NOTES

ANSWERS TO REVIEW QUESTIONS

1. False. The more specifically the effect is stated, the greater the potential for a quick and effective analysis.

2. False. Always review the rules.

3. Materials, methods, machines and people.

4. False. Always list all ideas during brainstorming.

5. False. Member participation is welcomed and encouraged.

6. c. No limit.

7. a, b, c.
   Staff ideas should be considered just like anyone else's. The group should not select an idea just because of who suggested it. Selecting ideas that generate discussion, but are not supported by data, can be a waste of time.

8. b. During voting.
   c. During verification. If a member has information that will affect the verification, the group should hear it.

9. a. Mandatory

10. c. Pareto analysis

11. 1. Large sheet of paper. Can be seen by everyone and provides a permanent record.
    2. Overhead projector. Can be seen by everyone. Does not take up much storage space.
    3. Blackboard. It can be seen, but a copy must be made to provide a record.
    4. Note pad. A note pad provides a record. It cannot be seen by everyone. Ideas tend to be repeated or forgotten. Note pads should be used only as a last resort.

© 1991 QCI INTERNATIONAL
REPRODUCTION PROHIBITED

227

6-27

BASIC CAUSE-&-EFFECT
ANALYSIS

NOTES

PROCESS
CAUSE-&-EFFECT
ANALYSIS

INTERNATIONAL
Red Bluff, CA 96080

MEETING NOTES

Process Cause-&-Effect Analysis

Prior to Meeting

- Review pages 233 through 263 of this chapter.

- Confer with facilitator.

- Post final agenda. A suggested agenda follows:

AGENDA
(Date)

Opening Activities
- Minutes.
- Status of action items.
- Review last training topic.
- Review milestone chart.

Today's Training Topic
- Review objectives.
- Present AV.

Discussion
- Review summary sheet.
- Discuss work sheet/review questions.

Closing Items
- Review action items.
- Set next meeting's agenda.

During Meeting

Prior to AV

* Welcome members and introduce guests.

* Review the posted agenda for today's meeting.

* Have the minutes of the last meeting read and approved.

* Ask for status report on any action items from previous meeting.

* Review and discuss the material on "Basic Cause-&-Effect Analysis." Discuss any completed work sheet exercises or redo some review questions if helpful.

* Introduce "Process Cause-&-Effect Analysis." Review objectives listed on page 233. You might have several members read them aloud.

During AV

* Present the AV module, stopping where the manual suggests and elsewhere if helpful.

After AV

* Get maximum involvement in a discussion of the material. Be sure to include a discussion of the topics on the summary sheet.

* Have the group answer and discuss some or all of the work sheet exercises and review questions at the end of this chapter.

* Review the objectives again. Ask members if they feel the objectives were met.

* Update milestone chart.

- Get member input in setting the agenda for the next meeting.

- Ask for volunteers to do action items.

- Suggest members read the chapter "The Management Presentation" before the next meeting.

- Announce the date, time and place of the next meeting.

- Thank attendees for their attention and cooperation.

- Adjourn the meeting.

After Meeting

- Meet with your facilitator to discuss the meeting.

- Follow up to make sure the minutes are completed and distributed.

- If possible, post the agenda for the next meeting in a place easily seen by members.

NOTES

Process Cause-&-Effect Analysis

OBJECTIVES

- To understand the differences and similarities between basic cause-&-effect analysis and process cause-&-effect analysis.

- To recognize how this technique can be used whenever a process is involved.

- To become familiar with the steps in using this problem analysis technique.

- To see how process cause-&-effect analysis can help save time by pinpointing the step in the process where the trouble is located.

---

1   (Graphic—can be substituted with organization logo)

2   (Credits)

233

PROCESS CAUSE-&-EFFECT ANALYSIS

Process cause-&-effect analysis can be used to analyze an entire process or a sequence of steps.

Review of Basic Cause-&-Effect

Before this variation is explained, a quick review of the basic cause-&-effect technique will be useful.

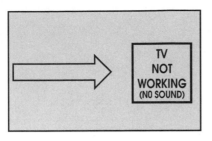

The effect, usually stated as a problem, is in the block to the right of the arrow. It is "TV Not Working—No Sound."

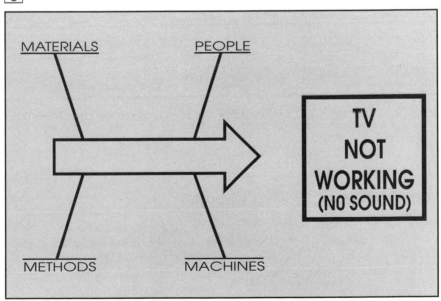

Team members suggest possible causes of that problem during a brainstorming session and list them to the left of the problem.

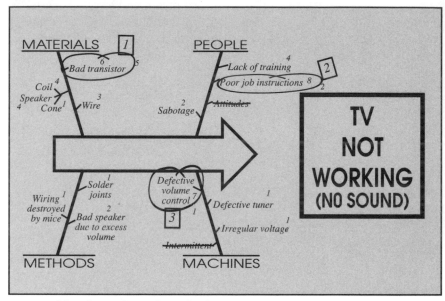

7

Members then identify the most important possible causes. These are circled and then prioritized. The completed diagram looks like this.

STOP THE AV

Test for understanding of basic cause-&-effect analysis.

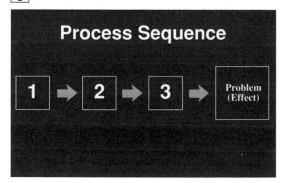

Process cause-&-effect analysis is similar in some respects to basic cause-&-effect analysis. There are, however, some important differences.

9 This technique involves several steps.

10

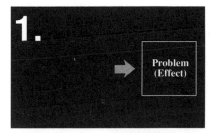

Step 1. State the problem as precisely as possible. (No difference here from basic cause-&-effect analysis.)

11

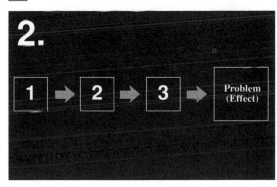

Step 2. Determine the process sequence. Adding this sequence is the difference between basic cause-&-effect and process cause-&-effect.

12 Usually, the process sequence is drawn, starting with the first step. Those that follow are listed one at a time.

13 But sometimes it is easier to work backwards.

*PROCESS CAUSE-&-EFFECT
ANALYSIS*

14   Let's work through an example using a problem that just might be easy to relate to—being late to work!

15

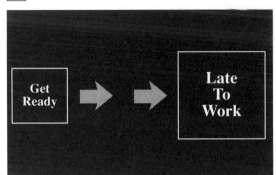

The first block in the sequence is labeled "Get ready." It includes what occurs from the time of waking up until the person is dressed.

16

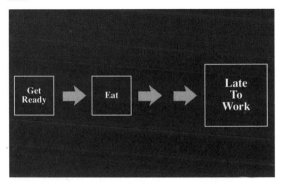

The second block is labeled "Eat," covering what takes place at breakfast.

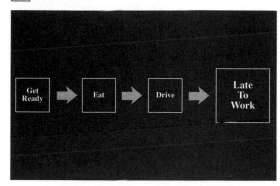

17

The final block in the sequence is labeled "Drive," to describe the task of driving to work.

18   An example in an office might be the excessive delays in the flow of certain paperwork. The flow of work can be identified easily. First, a draft is prepared. Next, it is printed. Finally, it is mailed.

19

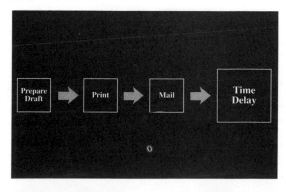

This process cause-&-effect diagram shows the sequence graphically.

239

PROCESS CAUSE-&-EFFECT
ANALYSIS

This process also applies just as well in a factory. For example, assume the metal is not adhering properly in a plating department. The sequence might be: First, dip the parts in the plating tank; second, dip them in the rinsing tank; and finally, air-dry them.

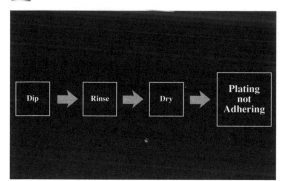

This process cause-&-effect diagram shows the sequence.

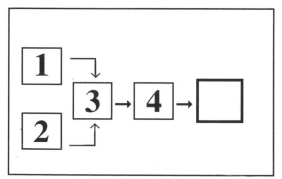

The blocks are usually in sequence, but occasionally one of the blocks is offset if that reflects how the process actually occurs.

23

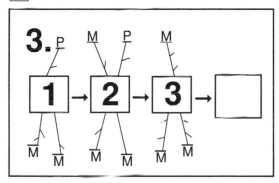

Step 3. Involve all members in a brainstorming session to identify possible causes.

24 Following certain rules makes brainstorming more productive. These rules are explained in detail in the brainstorming chapter. They include "go in rotation," "only one idea per turn" and "no evaluation during brainstorming."

25 After the rules have been read, the members can begin the brainstorming process.

26 Brainstorming moves quicker when the leader is assisted by a member who writes down ideas as they are called out.

27

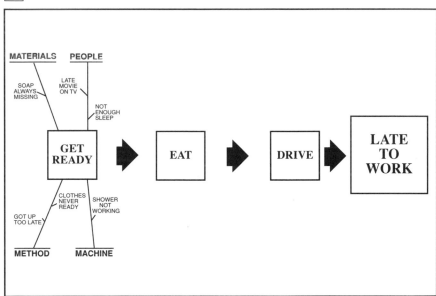

Back to the first example. Group members might first concentrate on the block titled "Get ready." Brainstorming is used during that step to identify possible causes for being late to work. Notice that cause categories such as the 3 M's and a P are also used.

28 After everyone says "Pass," members might move to "Eat" and brainstorm that block.

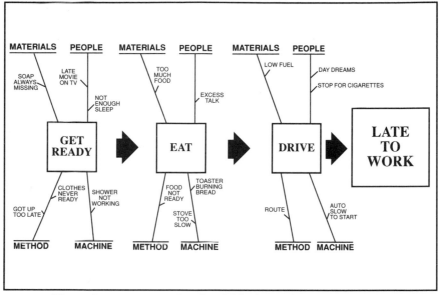

Then they move to the final block in the sequence. Brainstorming is completed when each person says "Pass."

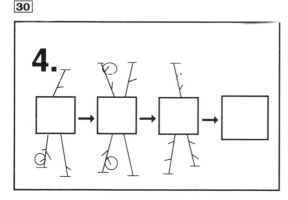

Step 4. Carefully consider the ideas collected during brainstorming to select the most likely causes.

Members must evaluate each cause. This could involve considerable time and detailed analysis.

© 1991 QCI INTERNATIONAL
REPRODUCTION PROHIBITED

243

7-11

PROCESS CAUSE-&-EFFECT
ANALYSIS

32 However, time is a luxury usually in short supply. Voting is comparatively rapid, and the results are usually impressive.

33 In this step, members will go through the first of two rounds of voting.

34

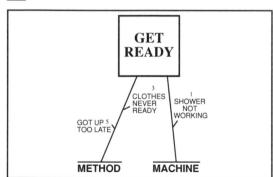

During the first round, members may vote for as many ideas as they wish. The vote is recorded on the diagram next to each cause. In this first round of voting, if more than one block has been brainstormed, members should vote on all causes, not just one block at a time. Remember, the leader also gets a vote. There is very little discussion during this round. Simply separate the major causes from the less important ones. If members need clarification on a particular idea, it is OK to stop the voting.

35 Next, circle the causes with the highest number of votes. Usually, this means at least two or three but could include more. Deciding on how many to circle is a judgment call by the team.

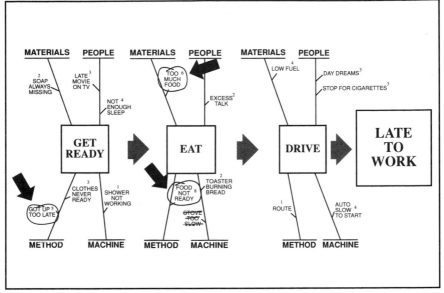

This diagram shows the major causes circled.

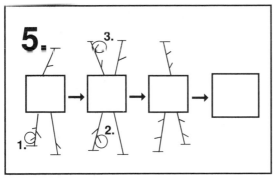

Step 5. Rank the causes circled in step 4 in order of importance. To accomplish this, examine only those causes that have been circled.

38   Members then vote on each circled cause. This is round 2. Members discuss each cause before voting.

39  When voting, consider anything that has changed as an excellent clue to discovering the true cause. Such is the case when this cook burns food for the first time.

40 Deviations from the norm also function as clues.

41 Recurring patterns also provide excellent clues.

42 After members discuss all circled items, they vote only on these major causes. Usually, each member can vote for only one of the circled causes.

43 The number of votes is jotted down next to each circled cause.

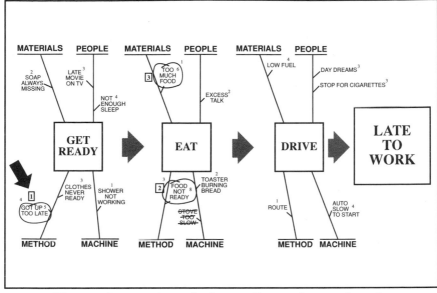

Then each cause is ranked according to the number of votes received. The highest vote-getter is the No. 1 most-likely cause. In our example this is "Got up too late."

STOP THE AV

Discuss the numbers beside the causes. This is a good opportunity to test the group for understanding.

45   A member may halt the voting at any time to argue for or against a cause. This can occur in either step 4 or step 5.

*PROCESS CAUSE-&-EFFECT
ANALYSIS*

46 **Step 6.** Test the No. 1 most-likely cause in order to verify it. Perhaps setting the alarm to go off earlier would verify that getting up too late is the true cause.

47 The No. 1 cause is the one to be verified. Some problems have only one cause and some have many causes. If a problem has many causes, group members may divide up the causes so that each one is studied. These would be tracked with an action log.

48 Members can use brainstorming to identify ways to verify.

49 Models can reduce verification cost. Members should make every effort to select a quick and inexpensive test.

50 An important follow-up to the verification step is the recommended solution.

51 Again, use brainstorming to identify various solutions.

52 The pros and cons of the top alternatives are debated by the members to achieve a consensus. One way to do this is to list the pros on one side of a chart and the cons on the other. Data is then collected concerning the costs and benefits of the top vote getters. Develop answers to the cons in case management asks during the presentation to management.

53 The selected solution becomes part of the presentation to management .

54

Keep several other points in mind.

Things To Remember

55

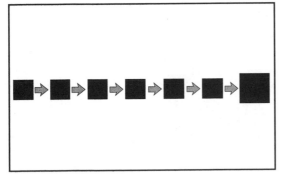

There is no limit to the number of blocks that can be used. Use as many as are necessary.

Basic cause-&-effect analysis and process cause-&-effect analysis are two variations of the same tool. The group should use only the one that fits the particular situation they are studying.

57

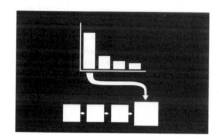

Often, the group selects the problem based on the results of a Pareto analysis.

58 During the brainstorming phase, group members concentrate on one block at a time rather than scatter their thoughts by jumping back and forth between blocks.

59

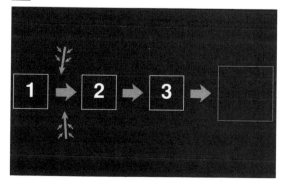

The members might decide to brainstorm what occurred between blocks, for example, during transportation. This is done in the manner indicated. If members had anticipated this step earlier, they could have added it as a separate block.

60 When members have determined the process steps, they may see a way to save time and effort during brainstorming. They may feel strongly that one particular block contains the source of the true cause.

61

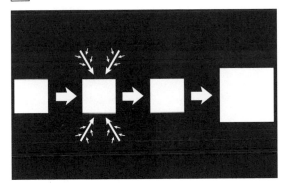

If so, brainstorming is centered on this block only. If the group is convinced it is on the right track, it may be unnecessary to do the other blocks.

62 The group does steps 4 and 5 while continuing to focus on the same block. Then members attempt to verify the principal cause they have selected.

STOP THE AV

Comment: Concentrating on one block only could cause group members to overlook the true cause.

Ask: Why then is it OK to do this at times?

Answers: 1. Since the members are experts, the probability is very high that the selected block does contain the true cause.
2. If they are wrong, they will discover this during verification.
3. The time saved is worth the risk.

PROCESS CAUSE-&-EFFECT ANALYSIS

63   Leader-directed discussion can sometimes be applied to either type of cause-&-effect analysis—basic or process.

STOP THE AV

Comment that the next series of frames introduces a special variation to Cause-&-Effect Analysis. Point out that the leader will rely greatly on use of the "5 W's and 1 H."

64   As mentioned in step 5, members may ask for clarification of one or more of the choices before the second voting round. So, the leader assumes control by asking a series of "what, why, when, where, who and how" questions that anyone may answer.

65

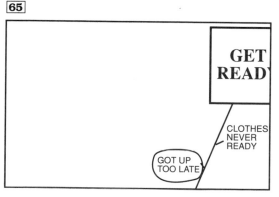

A major cause titled "Got up too late" illustrates this.

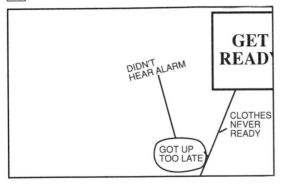

The leader asks, "Why did we get up too late?" A member responds, "We didn't hear the alarm."

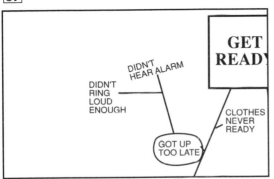

The leader questions, "Why didn't we hear the alarm?" A different member answers, "It did not ring loud enough."

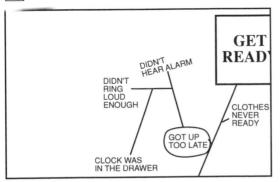

The leader asks, "Why?" The answer comes back, "The clock was in the drawer." This line of questioning can be continued for some time. It is an excellent way to expose the smallest details. Thus, the group members can be much more informed and confident as they proceed with the vote on whether "Got up too late" is the true cause.

© 1991 QCI INTERNATIONAL
REPRODUCTION PROHIBITED

253

7-21

*PROCESS CAUSE-&-EFFECT
ANALYSIS*

69 Leader-directed discussion should be conducted at a fast pace. It should not be done in rotation. Instead, members should quickly call out ideas in any order.

70 Should the group do the same for the other circled causes? Only if the members want a clearer understanding of them.

71 Finally, in the event the work is referred to at some future date, a legend should be included. It makes the document even more useful.

SUMMARY SHEET

Process Cause-&-Effect Analysis

Definition: Process cause-&-effect analysis is a technique used to analyze an entire process or a sequence of steps.

Process Cause-&-Effect Analysis Procedures:

Step 1. State the problem as precisely as possible.

Step 2. Determine the process sequence.

Step 3. Involve all members in a brainstorming session to identify possible causes.

Step 4. Carefully consider the ideas collected during brainstorming to select the most-likely causes.

Step 5. Rank the causes circled in step 4 in order of importance.

Step 6. Test the No. 1 most-likely cause in an attempt to verify it.

Comparison of Basic and Process Cause-&-Effect:

Steps	Basic	Process
1.	State Problem.	Same.
2.	Select major cause groups.	Determine the process sequence and select major cause groups for each step.
3.	Brainstorm.	Brainstorm each process block separately.
4.	Circle possible causes.	Same.
5.	Select true cause.	Same.
6.	Verify.	Same.

OTHER KEY POINTS:

A. In step 3, the rules of brainstorming should be stated prior to starting, even for experienced groups. Post the rules in the meeting room as a reminder.

B. Use a large sheet of paper. Avoid blackboards or note pads.

C. In the first round of voting, if members have brainstormed more than one block they should vote on all causes, not just one block at a time.

D. The No. 1 most-likely cause should be verified.

E. There is no limit on the number of blocks that can be used.

F. Members may decide to brainstorm what occurred between blocks—for example, during transportation.

G. It is possible that although the process may contain several blocks, only one will be brainstormed. This occurs when the group is convinced it has found the true cause within that one block.

WORK SHEET EXERCISES

1. Process cause-&-effect analysis can be used to advantage where several sequential steps occur. Such is the case in the problem of "Poor-tasting meal" at your home.

    ### Assignment

    Using the problem "Poor-tasting meal," identify the blocks involved in the entire sequence. To get started, use "Purchase meal ingredients" as your first block.

2. The process of identifying each block in the sequence often lends enough insight for you to choose one specific block to initiate brainstorming.

    ### Assignment

    In the "Poor-tasting meal" case, identify the block you would probably brainstorm first and explain your reasons.

3. Leader-directed discussion often proves effective in expanding the group's insight into one of the major causes that has been circled. Let us say such a major cause is "Lack of training."

Assignment

Assume you are the leader. Ask a series of at least three questions to open up or expand "Lack of training." Also, use your imagination to supply possible answers you might receive.

Question	Response

1.

2.

3.

REVIEW QUESTIONS

1. Name the two major types of cause-&-effect analysis.

   1._____

   2._____

2. Cause-&-effect analysis is just as effective for office and technical operations as it is for manufacturing areas.

   True _____   False _____

3. Leader-directed discussion can be used in both basic cause-&-effect and process cause-&-effect analysis.

   True _____   False _____

4. To avoid dissension during voting on the circled causes (second vote), it is best not to allow discussion.

   True _____   False _____

5. The leader's task involves creating a precise statement of the problem to be analyzed. Member involvement occurs only after brainstorming starts.

   True _____   False _____

6. In process cause-&-effect, members should identify the correct sequence of the blocks before creating a precise statement of the problem.

   True _____   False _____

7. In process cause-&-effect, members are not required to brainstorm each block in the same sequence the work is done.

   True _____   False _____

© 1991 QCI INTERNATIONAL
REPRODUCTION PROHIBITED

259

7-27

PROCESS CAUSE-&-EFFECT
ANALYSIS

8. Prior to the first round of voting, the leader should ask members to discuss the ideas suggested during brainstorming.

   True _____   False _____

9. Leader-directed discussion could be used prior to the final vote to get members thinking. Once things get rolling, the leader should return to the normal type of brainstorming or discussion.

   True _____   False _____

10. Leader-directed discussion is usually most effective when expanding some or all of the circled causes to gain in-depth insight into each cause prior to voting.

    True _____   False _____

11. In process cause-&-effect, during the brainstorming step, ideas may be directed at any block in the process. In other words, it is not necessary to brainstorm one block at a time.

    True _____   False _____

12. In process cause-&-effect, it is necessary to brainstorm all remaining blocks even though the group is certain it has discovered the true cause.

    True _____   False _____

ANSWERS TO WORK SHEET EXERCISES

1. There are many variations as to how this exercise could be answered. Any number of blocks could have been used. One possible answer is as follows:

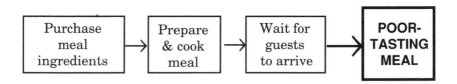

Another possible answer could be:

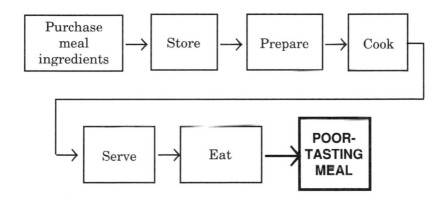

2. Since this is just a work sheet exercise, there is no one correct answer. To accurately pick the best block to brainstorm first, you would need to have actually experienced the situation. For example, if extraordinary delays occurred while waiting for guests to arrive, you might decide to start with that step.

PROCESS CAUSE-&-EFFECT
ANALYSIS

3. A possible dialogue could be as follows:

Question	Response
1. "Why is no training provided?"	"We don't have a classroom."
2. "Why is there no classroom?"	"It has never been budgeted."
3. "Why?"	"The boss opposes it."

ANSWERS TO REVIEW QUESTIONS

1. Basic
   Process

2. True

3. True

4. False. Discussion should be encouraged.

5. False. Get member involvement in precisely stating the problem.

6. False. The problem is stated first.

7. True

8. False. It will save an enormous amount of time to discuss only
   ideas the members want to explore or offer opinions on during
   the first round of voting. After the top vote-getters are circled,
   discuss all of them, pro and con, prior to your final vote.

9. True

10. True

11. False. It is preferable to concentrate everyone's energy on one
    block at a time

12. False. It may prove helpful, but time constraints may not allow
    this to occur easily.

© 1991 QCI INTERNATIONAL
REPRODUCTION PROHIBITED

263

7-31

PROCESS CAUSE-&-EFFECT
ANALYSIS

NOTES

THE
MANAGEMENT
PRESENTATION

INTERNATIONAL
Red Bluff, CA 96080

MEETING NOTES

The Management Presentation

Prior to Meeting

- Review pages 269 through 296 of this chapter.

- Confer with facilitator.

- Post final agenda. A suggested agenda follows:

AGENDA
(Date)

Opening Activities
- Minutes.
- Status of action items.
- Review last training topic.
- Review milestone chart.

Today's Training Topic
- Review objectives.
- Present AV.

Discussion
- Review summary sheet.
- Discuss work sheet/review questions.

Closing Items
- Review action items
- Set next meeting's agenda.

During Meeting

Prior to AV

- Welcome members and introduce guests.

- Review the posted agenda for today's meeting.

- Have the minutes of the last meeting read and approved.

- Ask for status report on any action items from previous meeting.

- Review and discuss the material on "Process Cause-&-Effect Analysis." Discuss any completed work sheet exercises or redo some review questions if helpful.

- Introduce "The Management Presentation." Review objectives listed on page 269. You might have several members read them aloud.

During AV

- Present the AV module, stopping where the manual suggests and elsewhere if helpful.

After AV

- Get maximum involvement in a discussion of the material. Be sure to include a discussion of the topics on the summary sheet.

- Have the group answer and discuss some or all of the work sheet exercises and review questions at the end of this chapter.

- Review the objectives again. Ask members if they feel the objectives were met.

- Update milestone chart.

- Get member input in setting the agenda for the next meeting.

- Ask for volunteers to do action items.

- Announce the date, time and place of the next meeting.

- Thank attendees for their attention and cooperation.

- Adjourn the meeting.

After Meeting

- Meet with your facilitator to discuss the meeting.

- Follow up to make sure the minutes are completed and distributed.

- If possible, post the agenda for the next meeting in a place easily seen by members.

NOTES

The Management Presentation

OBJECTIVES

- To understand why the group is likely to best communicate its recommendations and/or status to management using a presentation format.

- To realize that management channels must be respected and that the appropriate manager holds the ultimate authority to accept or reject the group's recommendation.

- To become familiar with the various chart formats and numerous presentation aids and equipment.

- To understand the importance of giving credit and appreciation to everyone who assisted the group in their project.

---

1   (Graphic—can be substituted with organization logo)

2   (Credits)

3

THE
MANAGEMENT
PRESENTATION

The presentation to management is an important and rewarding feature of group problem-solving activities. This chapter prepares the group to use this technique in the most effective way possible.

4 · It may be the first time members have had the opportunity to present their ideas to management.

5 · The presentation is a team effort. Everyone has participated in the analysis, and everyone should be encouraged to take part in the presentation.

THE MANAGEMENT
PRESENTATION
270
8-2
© 1991 QCI INTERNATIONAL
REPRODUCTION PROHIBITED

6 Communication is a prime reason for the presentation to management.

7 Why not simply submit a written recommendation? Some reasons include: It may be misunderstood, it lacks the impact of face-to-face, two-way communication, and it fails to adequately recognize the effort of members.

8

The members recommend solutions to the problems they have identified and analyzed.

9 Sometimes a presentation shows the status of a long, drawn-out problem that is still being worked on. Not only will this keep management informed, but it also often generates renewed enthusiasm among members.

THE MANAGEMENT
PRESENTATION

The meeting area should be kept free of distractions.

☐11

A checklist should be used to make sure everything is ready.

STOP THE AV

Ask: What are some of the items that could be on such a checklist?

Action: Use a flip chart (or an equivalent means) to construct a checklist from the group members' ideas. Typical items include:

- Invitations sent
- Sufficient chairs
- Extension cord
- Flip chart
- 35mm projector

- Screen
- Video monitor
- VCR player
- Name tents
- Overhead projector

12 The room should be set up ahead of time. Equipment should be in place and the charts ready to use.

13 A name card should be placed in front of each person, including members.

14 Starting at the scheduled time makes a good impression. However, if the manager is late, the group should probably wait until he or she arrives.

15

AGENDA	
Item	**Speaker**
1. Introduction	Bob
2. Problem Selection	Jeff
3. Data Collection	Don
4. Analysis	Bernie
5. Recommended Solution	Jack
6. Cost Justification	Jeff
7. Questions	All
8. Summary & Close	Bob

It is essential to have an agenda that lists the sequence of items and the speakers. Each attendee might be given a copy.

16   The agenda must set the direction for the course of the presentation, and it must be adhered to. Distractions must be avoided if possible.

STOP THE AV

Ask: Would the minutes be read at the management presentation?

Answer: No, minutes are not part of the management presentation.

---

17   Each member should be introduced at the presentation's beginning.

18   Each should again be introduced immediately before they speak.

19

Sometimes members can get the feeling of losing their audience. Visual aids can liven up a talk.

Use charts that illustrate the techniques members have mastered, such as Pareto and cause-&-effect. They make a good impression, and they get the message across quickly. Normally, charts prepared during the analysis need not be redone. It is simpler to use them as they are, and it also adds a note of realism.

21 Presentations can be made without any special aids. However, the speaker's effectiveness can increase if certain equipment is utilized.

22 It can be as basic as a flip chart.

23

Flip charts allow the room to remain brightly illuminated while material is presented.

24 Flip charts have an additional advantage—as each sheet is used, it can be hung on the wall for later referral by the speaker or others. Pre-number flip chart pages so they will be in order during the presentation to management.

25 *Everyone* in the room must be able to read the charts. Few things can turn off an audience like chart-wording that's too small to read.

26 An overhead projector can eliminate the need for large charts. Page-sized notes and charts can be quickly converted to an overhead transparency.

27 The group can use a slide projector to aid in the presentation.

28  Pictures are almost always more effective than words alone. The generous use of graphs can save an audience both frustration and time in understanding a message.

29   Many charts and graphs can be helpful.

30

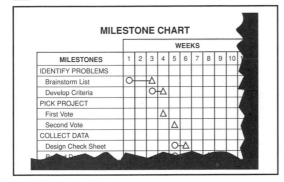

A milestone chart, sometimes called a Gantt chart, can help members to schedule and monitor activities. If a chart was used for the project, it should be shown during the presentation.

31   Line graphs are popular because they are easy to construct.

32   Bar charts also are familiar to almost everyone.

33

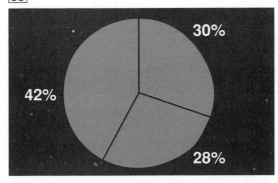

Pie charts visually depict the portions which make up the whole.

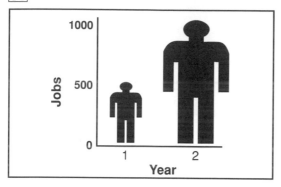

34

Pictographs can help. But one like this can mislead. The size of the large figure implies that jobs have quadrupled when in fact they have only doubled. The integrity of the user may well be questioned.

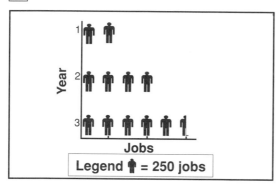

With this type of pictograph, the group can avoid the danger of misleading the audience. The final year demonstrates the use of a partial symbol.

General words cause different reactions in people. The word *pet* is an example. Members must be as specific as possible to prevent misunderstandings.

37

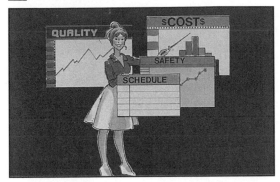

To get the group's message across, talk the audience's language. Achievements should be expressed, when practical, in terms of schedule, quality, cost and safety.

38 The KISS principle: Keep It Sweet and Simple. One highly successful executive practiced his presentations on younger members of his family to ensure that his speech was understandable and that he could capture and hold their attention.

39

If possible, bring an example of the actual hardware or paper and at the appropriate time let the audience handle and examine it. Few things work more effectively to get a message across.

40 If necessary, everyone can adjourn to the work area to witness the changes, or proposed changes, firsthand.

41 If a tour to the area is impractical, the group can show photographs or slide photos of the area.

42 Members can show a videotape of the actual operation or method to show the situation before and after changes are made.

43

Wait until the presentation is finished to give out handouts. Otherwise, management may find the material of more interest than the presentation.

44 Members should be proud of their achievements. They should talk about them. The audience wants to hear about their victories.

If a team has failed to solve an important problem and has decided to move on, should the members make a presentation to report on the failure? Of course! Edison conducted more than 3,000 experiments trying to build the light bulb. Rather than 3,000 failures, he said he had 3,000 victories because each test moved him closer to success. Even in projects that fail, there probably will be some positive features. Be sure to report on them as well.

46 It is OK to give the manager two or more choices and let the manager select from these alternatives. If this is done, members should be prepared to live with any option the manager selects.

47

Everyone who has helped the group should be thanked. It makes both them and the members look good, and it establishes the trust to ensure a continued win-win cooperation.

48 To what management level should members make the presentation? To the person or persons who can make the decision.

49

The group must not use the presentation to circumvent the normal chain of command to force a favorable response. That is not a win-win technique and will surely result in future problems.

50

Members should never put the manager on the spot with unexpected requests for solutions, funding or manpower increases. No surprises, please.

STOP THE AV

Ask: Why not make the presentation to top management (for example, to the steering committee)?

Answer: The normal reporting channels must be used.

Comment: If projects are truly selected from within the members' work area, their manager should be qualified to evaluate the recommendation.

---

51 Members should encourage questions to ensure the audience understands their message. The more confident members might even direct questions to the audience to ensure clear understanding.

52 Enthusiasm should show. It's contagious! However, this is often easier said than done. Many people tend to tense up and inhibit their actions when they speak to an audience. The solution? Practice. If you exaggerate in practice, it becomes easy to let your natural enthusiasm show in public.

53

A big smile relaxes both the speaker and the audience and allows enthusiasm to come through.

54

Gestures can add impact and clarity to the communication process. Practice will help perfect this skill.

55 Do not turn your back to audience members when you speak to them.

56 Cue cards containing key words effectively ensure portions of the talk will not be forgotten.

57

If preferred, a member may write out his or her presentation word-for-word. But if a speech is read, the speaker should frequently look up at the audience.

58 A dry run or two prior to the presentation is encouraged. The dry run eases tensions, and many problems and oversights are caught and corrected.

59 Some members may prefer to work in pairs during a presentation—this can build confidence.

60  What will be your group's next project? Usually, it has already begun. Before adjourning, have someone provide a brief status report, including a forecast of when the next project will be completed. The manager will be impressed, and it serves as a commitment that will stimulate member activity on the new project.

61 How frequently should the group make presentations to management? As often as necessary, but the group should strive for every three months. Sometimes more than one project is covered during a single presentation. For example, a small, completed group project, which doesn't require approval by the manager, might be described briefly.

62 Everyone benefits from this remarkable communication process—members, management and the entire organization.

63

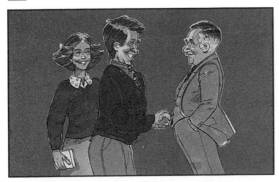 The presentation to management provides a splendid opportunity for members to communicate their ideas and achievements to management. It can be a rewarding experience for all!

*THE MANAGEMENT
PRESENTATION*

NOTES

SUMMARY SHEET

The Management Presentation

1. The presentation is a team effort—all members are encouraged to participate.

2. The meeting arrangements

   - A meeting area
   - Invitations sent
   - Sufficient seating for guests
   - Numbered cue cards
   - Equipment
   - Visuals, models, etc.
   - Name tents
   - Agenda

3. Use visuals that are readable and not misleading.

4. The group makes the presentation to the person or persons who can make the decision.

5. The presentation may be a status report.

6. Don't push for an answer from the manager at the presentation.

7. Strive for a presentation each quarter (every three months).

© 1991 QCI INTERNATIONAL
REPRODUCTION PROHIBITED

287
8-19

THE MANAGEMENT
PRESENTATION

NOTES

WORK SHEET EXERCISES

1. Imagine your team is preparing for a presentation to management. Both the team and the person to whom the presentation will be made probably will want others to attend.

   Assignment

   Construct a list of everyone who should attend the presentation, as well as anyone who might be interested. Briefly indicate why in each case.

2. **Assignment**

   Construct an abbreviated mock agenda. Use your imagination.

© 1991 QCI INTERNATIONAL
REPRODUCTION PROHIBITED

289

8-21

THE MANAGEMENT
PRESENTATION

3. Occasionally, a surprise occurs at a presentation to manage-
   ment. You are speaking when a manager (an invited guest) says,
   "One of my engineers recommended that solution two years ago.
   So what's new?"

   Assignment

   What do you respond?

REVIEW QUESTIONS

1. Presentations should be done by:

   a. The leader only
   b. The leader and assistant leader
   c. The leader and members

2. Charts used in the presentation need not be professionally prepared.

   True _____   False _____

3. The group uses presentations to make recommendations to management. Other reasons include:

   1._____

   2._____

4. The duration of the presentation to management should be:

   a. About 30 minutes
   b. About 60 minutes
   c. Only what is necessary

5. Identify at least four kinds of charts and graphs.

   1_____

   2._____

   3._____

   4._____

6. The chairperson for a presentation to management must always be the leader.

   True _____   False _____

© 1991 QCI INTERNATIONAL
REPRODUCTION PROHIBITED

291

8-23

THE MANAGEMENT
PRESENTATION

7. Presentations to management can highlight improvements in several general categories. At least three of these are:

1._____

2._____

3._____

8. The original cause-&-effect diagram might become messy as it is developed. It should be neatly redone prior to the presentation to management.

True _____   False _____

9. Name at least two methods (in addition to charts) that help management clearly understand your presentation.

_____

_____

10. Should the leader introduce each speaker, or should each speaker introduce the next one?

a. The leader
b. Each speaker
c. Optional

11. An advantage of a presentation to management is it allows us to invite highest-level managers and appeal directly to them for favorable decisions.

True _____   False _____

12. A presentation to management should begin at the specified time. One possible exception might be:

_____

_____

ANSWERS TO WORK SHEET EXERCISES

1. The following represents a list of possible attendees at a presentation to management and reasons it might be desirable for them to be there:

   - **Technical staff**—those who have helped with the project or will be affected by the project.

   - **Steering committee**—to view the work of the team. This helps the steering committee evaluate the program.

   - **The facilitator**—to help if the team gets in trouble.

   - **Visitors**—from your company or other companies, to see how teams operate.

   - **Non-members from the team's work area**—to see first-hand the team's work and proposed solution.

© 1991 QCI INTERNATIONAL
REPRODUCTION PROHIBITED

293

8-25

THE MANAGEMENT
PRESENTATION

2. The following abbreviated mock agenda is one of many examples that could be used.

Team Name _____

Date _____

PRESENTATION TO MANAGEMENT

1. INTRODUCTIONS
   Team members
   Guests
   People to whom the presentation is made

2. TOPIC
   Type of presentation: Recommended solution
                            or status report
   The project or problem: Selection process

3. THE PROCESS
   Data about project—collection methods
   Analysis—tools used
   Recommended solution
   Implementation plan
   Follow-up plan

4. DISCUSSION
   Questions & explanations

5. CLOSE
   Acknowledgments
   Adjourn

3. The following represent possible responses:

   • Things have changed from two years ago. Document with data.

   • We had the benefit of the input of many team members in thinking this project through.

   • We have had help from engineers (only if you really did).

ANSWERS TO REVIEW QUESTIONS

1. c. The leader and members

2. True

3. 1. Present status of current projects.
   2. Describe completed projects that did not need management approval.

4. c. Only what is necessary

5. Expect a variety of responses such as:

Line chart	Scatter diagram
Bar graph	Control chart
Column graph	Pareto chart
Pie chart	Histogram

6. False

7. Expect such answers as:

Quality	Attitudes
Schedule	Safety
Costs	

8. False. Too often, the neatly redone chart loses its believability.

9. Answers may include:

   Actual hardware
   Photographs
   Videotape demonstration
   A tour

10. c. Optional

11. False. Do not use the presentation to management to circumvent normal channels.

12. Answers might include:

    Your manager is late.
    A top executive has not arrived.

    In either event, it is probably wise to telephone the absent person's office before proceeding.

SUPPLEMENTARY INFORMATION

This final chapter contains a variety of information for the leader on the following subjects:

- Minutes
- Member Attendance
- Member Training
- Individual Group Accomplishments
- Project Summary Report
- Milestone Chart
- Action Log
- Process Flow Chart
- Steps in the Problem-Solving Process
- Keys to Successful Team Activities
- Team Performance Evaluation Checklist
- Future Training Topics to Keep Your Team Growing
- Example Code of Conduct Statements
- Measuring Results of Team Activities
- Project Selection Steps
- How to Make an Ordinary Team Extraordinary
- Be a Published Author in *Quality Digest*
- Leader Preparation for the Next Meeting
- Glossary of Terms and Definitions

APPENDIX A

RECORDS

Minutes

It is highly recommended that the group keep minutes for all employee involvement meetings. These minutes might be distributed to:

- Members
- The leader's supervisor
- Members of the steering committee (for new employee involvement teams)
- Facilitator
- Bulletin boards

The distribution should be listed on the minutes. Members become more motivated when they know their activities are being brought to the attention of others, such as managers.

For a new employee involvement team, the facilitator can be the recorder for the first few meetings. This gives the team members a chance to see what minutes look like and some time to select their own recorder. The facilitator should do this for only two or three meetings.

Minutes are a tool that should be used. They need to be taken, distributed and read at the next meeting.

Minutes

Name	Organization	Leader's Name

Attendees:

_____ _____ _____

_____ _____ _____

_____ _____ _____

_____ _____ _____

Minutes:

Action Items:

Recorder's Name		Date

Member Attendance

This form can be maintained by the leader, a member or the recorder.

The form accounts for the time members spend on a project and the total amount of time for employee involvement meetings.

The form also tracks each member's attendance. Low attendance for the group as a whole might mean the meeting is held at a bad time for the members. If one member's attendance drops, this could indicate his or her lagging interest.

The facilitator should receive a copy of this form.

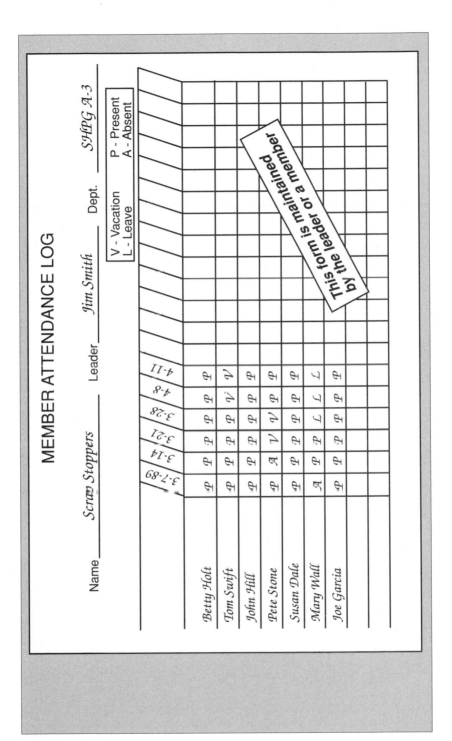

Member Training

This form is maintained by the leader or a member. It tracks the training level of each member and also the total amount of training of the group.

It can be used to do catch-up or combined training for members of several groups.

The facilitator should receive a copy of it.

See also: Additional Training

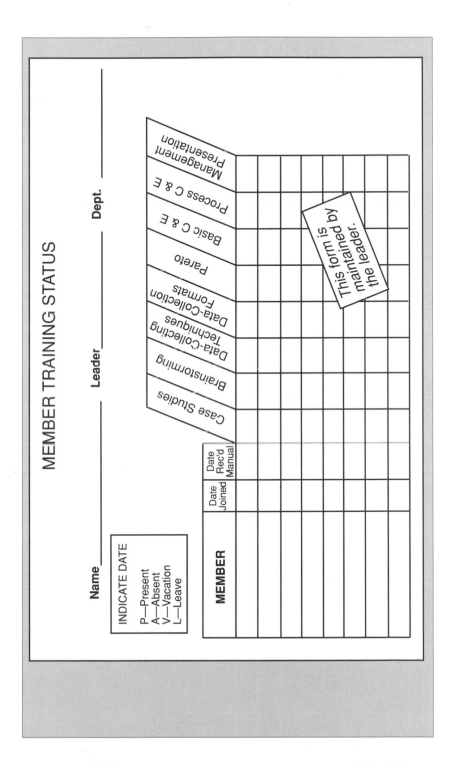

MEMBER TRAINING STATUS

Name _____ Leader _____ Dept. _____

INDICATE DATE

P—Present
A—Absent
V—Vacation
L—Leave

MEMBER	Date Joined	Date Rec'd Manual	Case Studies	Brainstorming	Data-Collecting Techniques	Data-Collection Formats	Pareto	Basic C & E	Process C & E	Management Presentation

This form is maintained by the leader.

Individual Group Accomplishments

This form is maintained by the leader with help from the facilitator. It is an ongoing record of the employee involvement team's achievements. It does more than inform others of the team's progress—it also informs the leader and members of how well they are doing.

Major projects, as well as the briefer "quick fix" or "quick kill" items, should be recorded.

Some teams will keep this record of accomplishments on a large sheet of paper and post it in the work area.

Copies should be given to the leader's supervisor, facilitator and in some cases the steering committee.

INDIVIDUAL GROUP ACCOMPLISHMENTS

Group Name _____ *'The Lending Ladies'* _____

Date Started	Leader	Project Description	Date Completed	Savings or Result
3-17-89	Jones	*Transposition of registration numbers on loan application. Investigation showed cause due to poorly designed loan form. Redesigned at time of regular reprinting at cost of $140.*	4-9-89	$3,240
4-2-89	Jones	*Malfunction of teller machines. Cause due to excessive buildup of heat because units were placed too close to wall.*	4-30-89	$8,660

This form is maintained by the facilitator or leader. It is an ongoing record of one group's achievements. It does more than inform others of accomplishments; it tells the leader and members how well they are doing. As each new item is added, make sure the facilitator (among others) receives a copy.

Project Summary Report

The project summary report is prepared by the leader or project coordinator with guidance from the facilitator. Essentially, it records the team project and the various actions members take to solve the problem. The following paragraphs describe how to use the report.

Indicate which persons and organizations members contacted and on what dates. Describe what analysis techniques members used.

Answer the questions regarding the management presentation, the manager's acceptance or rejection and implementation data.

In the section labeled RESULTS, list any measurable gains such as error rate decrease, scrap and waste reductions, decrease in customer complaints and dollar improvements.

In the same section, make note of attitude improvements, which are reflected by items such as reduced absenteeism and turnover and other morale-type indicators.

The audit summary should be done by a neutral party— perhaps someone in an official cost-evaluation group or maybe by the same person or group that evaluates employee suggestions. The auditor should be able to depend on cost information entered on the back side of this form by the leader, members, facilitator and others. Members should also complete a cost-benefit analysis of the project. This should be done even if the members need to estimate the costs and benefits.

The facilitator, and probably others, will receive a copy of the completed form. The facilitator, the leader's supervisor and any others involved with the project should also receive a copy of the completed form. People involved with the project might include employees from other departments who help work on the project or those who would be affected by implementation of the project.

PROJECT SUMMARY

_____ _____ _____

Title of Project _____

_____

Date Started _____ Date Completed _____

Summary of Actions Taken
(include individuals, organizations, dates, etc.)

Date of management presentation _____ Accepted? __ Implemented? __
If not accepted, why not?

RESULTS:
Measurable *(work related)*

Attitude Improvements

AUDIT SUMMARY *(work sheet of savings and expenses on back side)*

Total Estimated Savings $ _____

Total Costs _____

Savings _____

_____ _____ _____ _____
Auditor Organization Telephone Date

PROJECT SUMMARY

(Side Two)

Work Sheet

Various Estimated Costs as determined by leader, members, facilitator, etc.

Total
Costs [ ]

Estimated Savings as calculated by leader, members, facilitator, etc.

Total
Savings [ ]

Comments:

APPENDIX B

GOAL SETTING

Milestone Chart

The Milestone Chart, sometimes called a Gantt Chart, is a schedule. Team members often fear trying to schedule their project because they have inadequate information to do it right. They must remember all organizations live by schedules—schedules often constructed with sketchy and fragmented pieces of information. The point is, do the best with what you have—but do it!

Conditions are seldom static. Changes do occur. What if the realities of the schedule are altered? No problem. Simply make the appropriate changes, but label the revised schedule with a number and the revision date.

The group seldom reaches a goal in a single step. Usually, several action steps are required. Involve members in determining what the steps will be. A first step might be "Determine the present error rate." A second step could be "Design a check sheet to tally and categorize errors."

MILESTONE CHART

MILESTONES	1	2	3	4	5	6	7	8	9	10	11	12	13	14	15	16	17	18	19	20	21
IDENTIFY PROBLEMS																					
Brainstorm List	O		△																		
Develop Criteria			O	△																	
PICK PROJECT																					
First Vote				△																	
Second Vote					△																
COLLECT DATA																					
Design Check Sheet					O	△															
Record Data					O		△														
ANALYZE DATA																					
Pareto Analysis							O	△													
C &-E Analysis									O	△											
DEVELOP SOLUTIONS																					
Brainstorm Solutions											O	△									
PICK BEST SOLUTIONS																					
Criteria/Voting												O	△								
Cost/Benefit													O	△							
IMPLEMENT SOLUTIONS																					
Develop Plan															O	△					
Mgmt. Presentation																			△		
FOLLOW UP																					
Monitor																					O

Action Log

Teams should get in the habit of using an action log to keep up with project assignments. The log should be updated as a regular part of each meeting.

Here is one example of an action log. You can create your own format to fit your specific project. This form could be either a part of your minutes or a separate item.

Action Item #	Action	Who will do it	Planned Date	Actual Date	Result

This log allows both test results and solutions to be entered. In Japan, the term "countermeasures" is usually used in place of "solutions." Both terms mean the same thing.

Project action logs are most effective in working with chronic problems, which may have many small solutions over a long period of time.

APPENDIX C

VARIOUS

Process Flow Chart

During a project, team members perform three major activities: they identify, analyze and solve problems. Each activity has one or more steps which team members need to consider. One approach that many teams use is shown below.

Team Problem-Solving Process

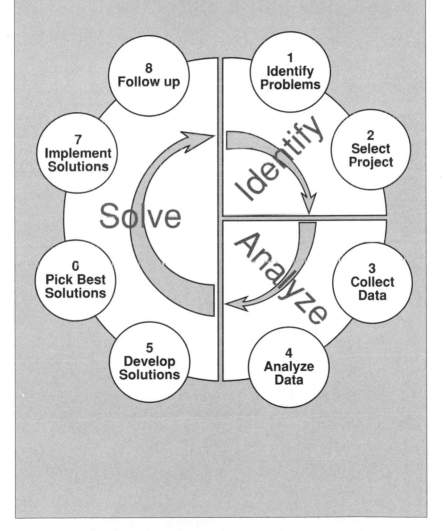

Steps in the Problem-Solving Process

Steps	Examples of Commonly Used Tools
1. Identify problems.	Brainstorming
2. Select project.	Voting Discussion Criteria
3. Collect data.	Sampling Check sheets Checklists Drawings
4. Analyze data.	Pareto Cause-&-effect analysis
5. Develop solutions.	Brainstorming
6. Pick best solution(s).	Voting Discussion Criteria
7. Implement solution(s).	Presentation to management
8. Follow up.	Sampling Check sheets Checklists Drawings

Keys to Successful
Team Activities

- Substantial study and planning are done before starting and expanding.

- Management is actively and visibly supportive.

- A functioning steering committee oversees the effort.

- A working coordinator is assigned.

- Substantial effort is made to sell benefits of participation.

- Appropriate training is provided at all levels.

- Teams are assigned a facilitator who serves mainly as a process coach.

- Teams focus on problems or issues within a clearly defined scope.

- Team members have expertise specifically related to the scope for which their team has been organized.

- Teams complete all steps of a prescribed process.

- People-building is emphasized but balanced with a concern for tangible results.

- Teamwork is encouraged; faultfinding and competition are discouraged.

- Recognition is provided in a sincere and timely manner.

Team Performance Evaluation Checklist

This kind of checklist can be a useful tool for teams. One way to use it is to complete one after every meeting. This could be done by the group, the leader or the facilitator.

A second approach would be to use it for a periodic evaluation. For example, each team might be evaluated twice a year. Again, it could be done at the team, leader or facilitator level.

Example of
Team Performance
Evaluation Checklist

_____ Was there a prepared agenda?

_____ Were new members or guests introduced?

_____ Has the leader attended leader training classes?

_____ Is there an assistant leader who has attended leader training?

_____ Have all team members received training?

_____ Are team records being maintained?

    _____ Minutes

    _____ Attendance

    _____ Training

    _____ Project status

_____ Does the team have a code of conduct?

_____ Does the leader do a good job of involving everybody?

_____ Does the team do a presentation to management every three months?

_____ Are aids such as projectors, TVs, blackboards, flip charts and tape recorders available?

Future Training Topics to Keep Your Team Growing

- Histograms

- Control Charts

- Stratification Techniques

- Scatter Diagrams

- Process Control Analysis

- Problem Selection

- Cost-Benefit Analysis

- Force Field Analysis

- Implementation Planning

- Team Effectiveness Skills

- Process Analysis

- Project Goal Setting

- Group Motivation and Incentives

QCI offers training and training materials on all of these topics. Let us help you increase your problem-solving power.

Example Code of Conduct Statements

Many groups find it helpful to develop a code of conduct, which includes rules or guidelines that all members agree to follow. Some example statements other groups have used include:

- Attend all group meetings and be on time.

- Listen to and respect the views of other members.

- Criticize ideas, not people.

- Accept results of group votes.

- Everyone is equal during team meetings.

- The only stupid question is the one that isn't asked.

- Carry out assignments on schedule.

- Give credit to those to whom it is due.

- Show appreciation to non-members who give assistance.

- Avoid criticism and sarcasm toward others' ideas.

- No disruptive side conversations.

- Always strive for win-win situations.

- Don't belittle the others' ideas or opinions.

- Before you criticize, give praise and honest appreciation.

Use the following space to reword some of the above statements or to create others you think should be considered by your group:

_____

_____

Measuring Results of Team Activities

The following questions can stimulate ideas:

ASK:
- What are some general categories in which to measure team progress?
  Common answers: quality, cost, attitudes, safety.

ASK:
- Why express team results in terms of quality?
- In what ways can quality be measured?
  Common examples: defects, errors, rework, spoilage, customer complaints, meeting schedules.
- Where can we get this type of information in our organization?
- Who specifically could help provide information on quality?

ASK:
- How can costs be measured?
  Common answers: savings-to-cost ratios, net savings, learning curves, standard hours, material costs.
- How will we know the number of man-hours being expended by team members and others who occasionally assist them?
- What departments could help us determine labor and material costs?
- Who in our organization is officially responsible for evaluating cost savings?

ASK:
- Should we try to measure attitudes related to teams?
- How can attitudes be measured?
  Common answers: absenteeism, tardiness, turnover, grievances, surveys.
- Can we attach dollar amounts to any of these attitude measures?
- Who could help us do that?
- Can testimonials be used to measure the success of teams? CAUTION: Badly administered surveys will provide misleading results.

ASK:
- What team results might not be measurable?
  Some examples: safety improvements, problem prevention.
- Should we post charts that summarize completed team projects?

Project Selection Steps

1. Clearly define the topic to be brainstormed.

   Examples:

   "Quality problems in our own work area"
   "Paperwork problems in our own work area"
   "Maintenance problems in our own work area"
   "Production problems in our own work area"
   "Safety problems in our own work area"

2. Occasionally remind members of the topic during brainstorming.

   Example:
   When moving to a new sheet of paper say, "OK, we're brainstorming for quality problems in our own work area."

3. Develop a list of criteria for the group's next project.

   Example:

   ### Criteria For Our First Project
   - Relatively easy
   - Short time frame
   - No outside help required
   - Measurable
   - Affects all members
   - Data is easy to get

4. Occasionally remind members of the purpose of the vote during the first round.

   Examples:
   "How many of you think this would be a good first project?"
   "How many of you think this item meets our criteria?"

5. After circling items that received the most votes, reword or remove items not stated as problems.

   Examples of incorrect problem statements:

Implied solutions:	Solution statements:
"Lack of . . ."	"Get . . ."
"We need . . ."	"Buy . . ."
"Not enough . . ."	"Clean up . . ."

6. Use the criteria list from step 3 to stimulate discussion prior to the final vote.

How To Make an Ordinary Team Extraordinary

(The key things your team should have been or should be doing.)

1. Create an action log for each project.

2. Construct a milestone chart for each project.

3. Develop a code of conduct.

4. Use the project selection steps.

5. Post the rules of brainstorming.

6. Follow the eight-step problem-solving cycle.

7. Verify causes.

8. Give the status of your next project at the presentation to management.

9. Invite your manager(s) to your meeting at least once a month.

10. Use an agenda.

11. Record concise minutes for each meeting.

12. Make a presentation to management every three months.

13. Post a list of your team's accomplishments.

14. Fill out the project summary form.

15. Say "thanks" to everyone who has helped.

Be a Published Author in
Quality Digest

Quality Digest is a monthly magazine that features articles on subjects relating to the general topic of quality improvement.

You Can Be a Published Author

Manuscripts should be typed, doubled-spaced on standard letter-size paper. Articles usually are between five to 12 pages long.

All pages should be numbered. All accompanying material, whether drawn figures or photographs, should be explained.

Black-and-white or color photos should be glossy prints with good contrast (8" x 10" B & W glossies are best). Do not send slides. Captions should be lightly penciled in on the backs of prints so no damage is caused.

Call First to Discuss Your Idea If You Wish

The Digest staff can give you guidance and ideas to help you get your story in print. If you don't want to write a full-length article, you could write a short news item or a guest editorial.

Leader Preparation for the Next Meeting

Good meetings do not just happen. They are the result of careful planning. The following lesson plan, filled in by the leader ahead of time, can make an otherwise ordinary training meeting sparkle! Until the leader is comfortable with doing this sort of pre-planning, it is wise to seek guidance from the facilitator.

LESSON PLAN

Date _____

Subject: _____

Objectives: _____

_____

_____

_____

Plan:

　Introduction _____

_____

　Presentation
　Stop #　Slide　　Comment or Question

　_____　_____　　_____

　_____　_____　　_____

　_____　_____　　_____

　_____　_____　　_____

　_____　_____　　_____

　_____　_____　　_____

　_____　_____　　_____

　_____　_____　　_____

　Practice Exercise:_____

_____

　Review:_____

_____

Training Aids _____

Glossary of Terms and Definitions

Brainstorming

Brainstorming generates ideas. There are many methods of brainstorming. The method described in this text involves all group members. Each member gives one idea per turn in rotation. The ideas are written on a large piece of paper where everyone in the group can see them. The process continues until all members pass.

Basic Cause-&-Effect Analysis

Cause-and-effect analysis is a popular problem-solving tool. In this technique, the problem to be analyzed is stated in a box to the right. Possible causes are listed by major sub-groups in the area to the left. Members test possible causes to find out which ones are true causes.

Control Charts

Control charts are line graphs with control limits added. Control limits are shown as dotted lines. They show how much variation is present in the process being charted. If plot points stay within control limits, the process is said to be "in control." This does not mean the product is acceptable. The team would only know this by comparing the process output to the specifications.

Deming, Dr. W. Edwards

Dr. Deming is an American statistician who assisted the Japanese in gaining a high level of competency in statistical quality control from the late 1940s through the 1970s. He is recognized as the father of modern productivity in Japan and is having a strong influence on Western industry into the 1990s. The widely acclaimed Deming Prize is awarded to those companies and individuals who achieve high standards of the Deming award committee. The prize recognizes outstanding achievements in the field of statistical quality control.

Facilitator
The facilitator, the primary resource person for employee involvement teams, observes the process and assists the leader in keeping the group on target. The facilitator coordinates the activities of all involvement teams and is usually a steering committee member.

Group Dynamics
The interpersonal exchanges and processes that take place among small-group members are examples of group dynamics.

Histogram
A histogram is a bar graph that shows the frequency distribution of whatever is being measured. The vertical axis is usually the frequency or number of each value. The horizontal axis is the value.

Ishikawa, Dr. Kaoru
The late Dr. Ishikawa, who was a university professor in Japan, is considered the father of quality control circles. Most employee involvement activities trace their roots to quality control circles. His pioneering efforts were largely through the Union of Japanese Scientists and Engineers (JUSE).

JUSE (Union of Japanese Scientists and Engineers)
JUSE, a non-profit association headquartered in Tokyo, has played a leadership role in helping Japan gain its outstanding reputation for quality. In 1962, JUSE persuaded member companies to experiment with the quality circles concept. They have maintained their leadership position regarding quality circles since that time.

Leader
The group leader is chosen from among the members. Typically, the first leader is the supervisor of the work group from which the team is drawn.

Management Presentation
Group members present recommended solutions to their manager in a presentation format. Various members take turns explaining the analyses they used to complete their project.

Normal Distribution
The normal distribution is a mathematical form which is bell-shaped—sometimes called a bell curve. It contains the same area on either side of its highest point and sets control limits for control charts. Many things in nature are distributed in the shape of a normal curve. This makes it valuable as a prediction tool.

Pareto
A Pareto graph is a bar chart with the columns arranged in descending order from the left. Each column represents a different problem or situation. The tallest, which is on the left, is No. 1 in importance and is usually handled first by the group. In Pareto analysis, members use Pareto charts to prioritize problems.

Pilot Program
The introduction of an employee-participation concept into an organization is normally done on a pilot basis. That is, a limited, manageable number of groups are begun, usually three to six groups. They operate for a predetermined length of time—four to six months is common—and evaluated. The pilot phase provides valuable insight into modifications that should be made prior to expanding the concept to others.

Presentation to Management (Refer to Management Presentation)

Process Cause-&-Effect Analysis
Process cause-&-effect analysis closely resembles basic cause-&-effect analysis. It differs in one major aspect. The steps in the process are broken out and clearly identified to give group members greater insight into the process they are diagnosing. This technique is ideal for use on an assembly line or anywhere else where things happen in a certain sequence.

Productivity

Productivity is often referred to as a measure of output over input. It frequently determines management effectiveness in using the various resources available. In group activities, it often refers to members getting more done by working smarter, not harder (not a speedup). Productivity gains by groups frequently result from reducing the number of errors in the work they are doing, thus reducing the amount of rework. Scrap also is often reduced.

Scatter Diagram

A scatter diagram is a useful analytical tool. It shows the relationship between two variables in graphic form. An example is weight vs. volume.

Steering Committee

The steering committee is often considered the "board of directors" for employee involvement activities. It is usually made up of management-level people from different areas in the organization. It also may include non-management people. This group provides guidance and direction for team activities.

Stratification

Stratification is the process of taking a problem apart and examining each part separately. For example, errors may be occurring at an excessive rate in a large department. It may be best to separate the errors into the subgroups within the department and analyze each group separately. It is quite possible the problem is isolated to one area.